Breeding
and Growing

MICHAEL CHINERY B.A.

FOUNDATIONS OF SCIENCE LIBRARY

GREYSTONE PRESS/NEW YORK · TORONTO · LONDON

This new presentation assembles freshly edited material from
'Understanding Science' on one subject into a single volume.

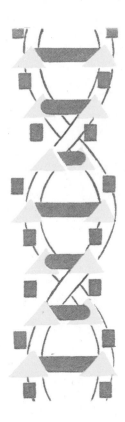

Contents

Cells and Chromosomes

CHAPTER ONE

The Microscopic Structure of Cells

IN 1667 Robert Hooke used a primitive type of microscope to examine some thin pieces of cork. He saw that the cork was made up of tiny units which he called 'cells'. All plant tissues are made up of cells, each having a definite boundary wall of cellulose. Animal tissues lack cellulose walls and the units are less obvious. The term 'cell' is applied to them, however, for it is clear that the contents of each unit are far more important than the boundary. It is within the cell that the vital processes of life are carried out.

The basis of all living cells is protoplasm. It is important to realise that this is not a single substance; it is a very complicated mixture of organic and inorganic substances in which chemical changes are continuously taking place. The chemical composition of protoplasm therefore varies not only between species and between cells performing different functions but also in individual cells at different times. The main component is water in which there are suspended or dissolved numerous *proteins*, *lipids* (fatty substances), *carbohydrates*, and inorganic salts. The electron microscope shows that there is an elaborate system of fibres and channels within the protoplasm.

Every cell is bounded by a *cell-membrane*. This is not an external structure but a living part of the cell. The membrane can be seen with the aid of the electron microscope and much other evidence points to

its importance. Cells placed in liquid surroundings do not mix with the liquid unless they are pierced with a very fine needle. This suggests some sort of envelope for the

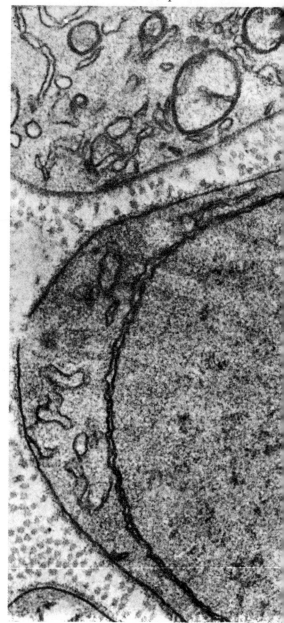

This is a reproduction of an electron microscope photograph of a section of a nerve. The technique shows clearly the large Schwann cell and its nucleus. The layered arrangement of the myelin sheath formed by the Schwann cell membrane around the nerve fibre is clearly shown. n.f. = nerve fibre, n.m. = nuclear membrane of Schwann cell, m.s. = myelin sheath.

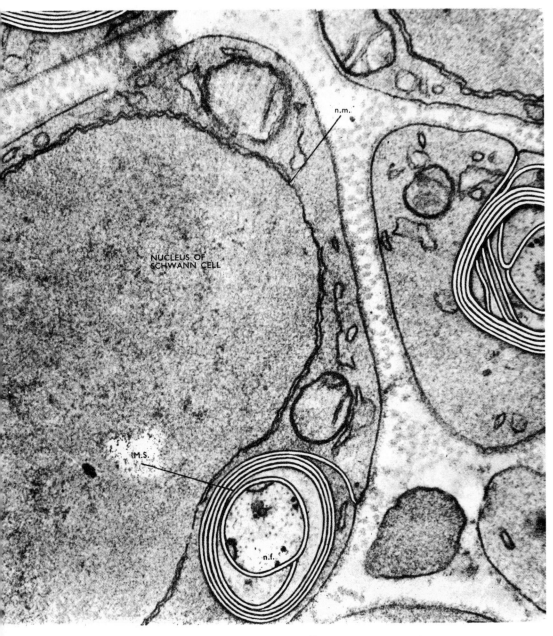

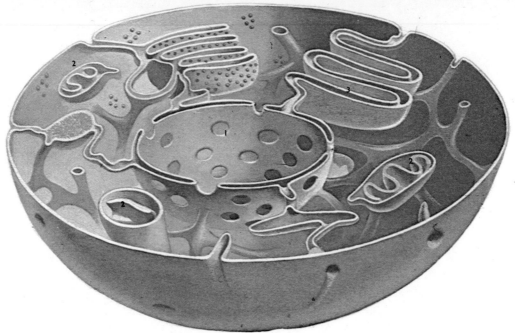

A diagram of half a cell showing the nucleus (1), *mitochondria* (2), *Golgi apparatus* (3) *and endoplasmic reticulum.*

protoplasm. Research indicates that the cell membrane surrounding the protoplasm consists of a network of protein and lipid (fatty) material which prevents loss of the cell contents and also allows some flexibility. The thickness of this cell membrane layer is less than one thousandth of a millimetre.

The cellulose cell walls of plants are external to this cell membrane and give the cell a regular shape. The shape of cells may be controlled by external factors. In animals the shape may be decided by the pressure of the other cells. Many protozoans have rigid coverings which maintain a fixed shape. Others, like *Amoeba*,

continually change their shape. Protozoans have been called unicellular (single-celled) animals and directly compared with cells of other animals. This is, however, not possible; in higher animals no cell performs all the functions, as a protozoan does. It may be better to call protozoans *accellular* (lacking cells) because their bodies are not divided into cells.

Cell contents

Apart from the protoplasm almost all living cells have other structures in common of which the *nucleus* is best known. This structure controls the whole cell and as a rule there is only one nucleus in each cell. It consists of special proto-

Some protozoans showing typical structures.

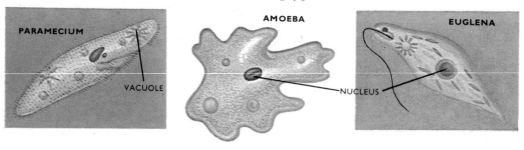

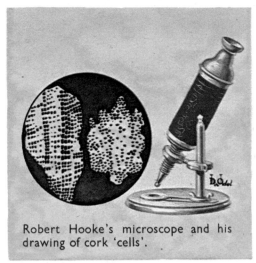

Robert Hooke's microscope and his drawing of cork 'cells'.

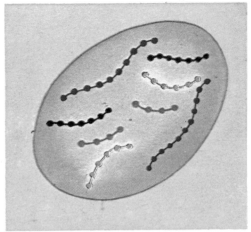

The structure of chromosomes within a nucleus. Only four pairs are shown. Each bead represents a gene of which there may be thousands on each chromosome. Each chromosome can be paired with another similar one.

plasm (*nucleo-plasm*) which contains certain substances (nucleo-proteins and nucleic acids). These regulate the manufacture of the proteins of the rest of the cell protoplasm (cyto-plasm). Surrounding the nucleus is a membrane similar to that around the whole cell. There is a darker region within the nucleus called the *nucleolus*.

The majority of cells are penetrated by a system of canals, the *endoplasmic reticulum*. This probably serves to transport materials from the surface to the inner parts of the cytoplasm.

With special staining techniques the *Golgi apparatus* can be demonstrated. This is a collection of protein and fatty material which forms coiled tubular bodies usually in the region of the nucleus. The Golgi apparatus is found in almost all animal cells and although its function is not known it must play some important part in the metabolism of the cell.

Scattered throughout the cytoplasm (but occasionally in concentrated patches) there are numerous tiny rod-shaped particles called *mitochondria* (mite- o- con- dria). These have been examined in living and dead material and are composed of protein lipid just like many of the other cell components. Research in recent years has shown that they carry on the cells respiratory mechanisms – which give the energy for processes such as growth.

Plastids are common inclusions in plant cells but are rarely found in animal tissue. They are modified regions of cytoplasm which contain pigments and other materials used in the production of food material. Those containing chlorophyll are called *chloroplasts*.

The above-mentioned structures all play some part in the chemical metabolism of the cell but there are a number of cell inclusions which are not directly concerned with cytoplasmic activity. In many epithelial cells (*e.g.* those lining the intestine) and gland cells there are numerous *secretory granules* which release chemical substances (hormones, enzymes, etc). The origin of the granules is still not understood. Food is stored in cells as oil droplets or as grains of starch or other carbohydrate material. These food reserves are released and used

9

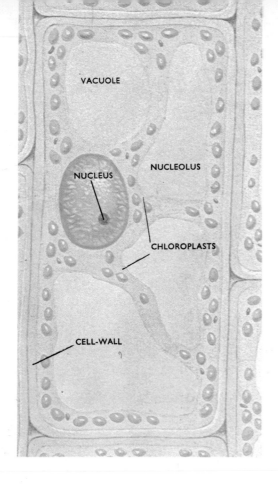

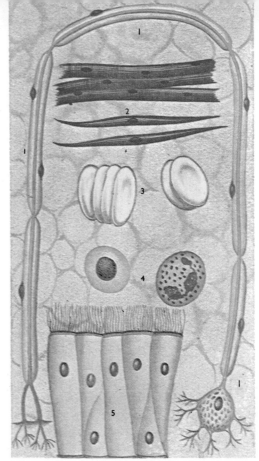

Some typical animal cells.

(1) *A single nerve fibre* (2) *Muscle fibres* (3) *Red Blood Corpuscles* (4) *White Blood Corpuscles* (5) *Epithelial (lining) cells from the windpipe.*

A typical plant cell.

when required. *Vacuoles* are fluid-filled spaces within cells. They are most common in plant cells where they may be very large. The cell-sap contained may be a food and water reserve or a collecting point for excretory material. Other inclusions in the cell include pigment granules and yolk grains (in egg cells).

The Chromosomes

The nucleus has been mentioned as being the controlling body of the cell. It controls not only the working of the cell but also its formation and structure. The nucleoplasm contains a certain amount of denser material which at certain periods

(associated with the reproduction of the cell) becomes clearly visible (under the light microscope) as coiled threads. These are the chromosomes. With certain important exceptions every cell nucleus in the human body has 46 chromosomes. Each one can be matched with one other and there are in fact 23 pairs of chromosomes. In the male there are more correctly 22 pairs and two odd chromosomes. Mouse cells contain 20 pairs while pea-plant cells contain 7 pairs. Thomas Morgan and later workers experimenting with the fruit fly *Drosophila* found that it has very large chromosomes in its salivary glands.

CHAPTER TWO

Outline of Genetics

AN INTRODUCTION TO GENETICS

Imagine four eggs. Each has a shell, a white, and a yolk. The eggs are about the same size and weight. When the embryos (the embryo is that part of the egg which develops into the new animal) start to grow they will be, at first, indistinguishable. But when the animals are fully developed they are very different.

The science of *genetics* deals with the question of how it is decided that each of these eggs will develop into a different kind of animal.

Broadly speaking, there are two sets of factors that decide how an egg will develop: external (outside) factors, such as light, temperature, food supply; and internal factors, which may be thought of as a set of *instructions*.

There are many instances of external factors that affect development: temperature can decide

whether a shrimp's eyes will be red or black; temperature governs coat colour in Himalayan rabbits; and food quantity and quality affect the weight and physical appearance of many animals, including Man.

It is clear, however, that external factors have limits: a crocodile egg placed in a hen coop still develops into a crocodile, while a change of diet will not alter the sex of the chicken.

External factors are often easy to find and to measure and we can usually obtain a fairly clear idea of how they operate. Internal factors

A simplified diagram of a section through a hen's egg.

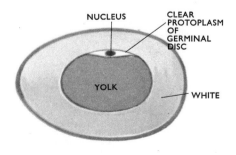

NUCLEUS CLEAR PROTOPLASM OF GERMINAL DISC

YOLK

WHITE

MALE LEGHORN

FEMALE LEGHORN

FEMALE RHODE ISLAND RED

MALE CROCODILE

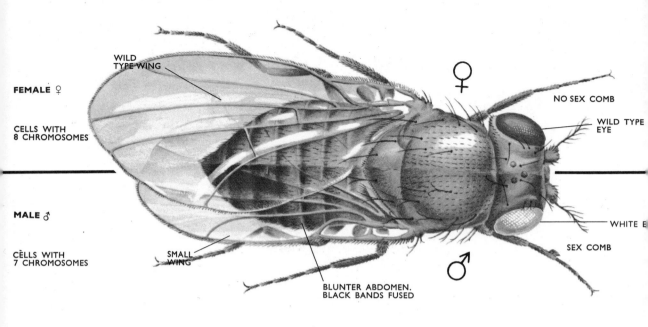

FEMALE ♀

WILD TYPE WING

CELLS WITH 8 CHROMOSOMES

NO SEX COMB

WILD TYPE EYE

MALE ♂

CELLS WITH 7 CHROMOSOMES

SMALL WING

BLUNTER ABDOMEN. BLACK BANDS FUSED

WHITE E

SEX COMB

are a much more difficult problem. The eggs were almost identical in appearance and even the young embryos were very similar. If there are such things as internal instructions, where are they?

The differences are not apparent to the naked eye. They may be observable with the aid of a microscope, or they may be invisible chemical differences. An important clue discovered during this century lies within the nucleus of the cell. It can be shown that the nucleus contains threads called *chromosomes*. The number of chromosomes in the nucleus of the crocodile's egg differs from that in the nucleus of the hen's egg. Could the chromosomes be the instructions? If so, one would expect to find a different number of chromosomes in the different types of chicken, but this is not so – all chicken eggs have the same number of chromosomes in their nuclei. Do we therefore reject the idea that chromo-

somes could be instructions for development?

In most animals and plants the number of chromosomes is an even one – 46 in Man, 8 in fruit flies (*Drosophila*) – and it is possible to identify pairs of chromosomes of similar length and structure. Man has 23 pairs; fruit flies have 4 pairs. In fact, only the female human has 23 pairs: the male has 22 pairs plus 2 odd chromosomes. The fruit fly male has 3 pairs plus 2 odd chromosomes.

In birds the pattern is reversed and the females have the two odd chromosomes. The interesting point here is that whether a fertilized egg develops into a *male* or a *female* depends on the chromosome difference. This supports the theory that chromosomes are instructions.

Further evidence for this theory is provided by very strange cases of development in fruit flies where one half of the body is male and the other half is female. Examination of the nuclei in the cells of such insects reveals that the nuclei in the male half have 7 chromosomes, while those in the female half have 8 chromosomes. Animals that are half male and half female are called *gyandromorphs*.

But the two hens illustrated at the beginning of this chapter have exactly the same number of chromosomes and yet they are quite different. Thousands of instructions are necessary for the development of even a small animal and so one chromosome obviously cannot give just one instruction. Perhaps each chromosome is, so to speak, a book of instructions and, like a book, may contain a large number of individual instructions. In order to develop these ideas further, we must take a look at Man's first attempt to unravel the mysteries of inheritance: we must look at the work of Gregor Mendel.

THE WORK OF GREGOR MENDEL

Gregor Mendel was the first person to establish some sort of system in the field of genetics. He was a monk and taught science at a school in Brunn—now part of Czechoslovakia —in the middle part of the nineteenth century. The principles that Mendel discovered hold good today and form the basis of the Science of Genetics which has practical value in plant and animal breeding.

Mendel experimented with garden peas which he grew in the garden of his monastery. He noticed that not all the plants were alike: some were tall, others short; some seeds were round while others were wrinkled. These characters were clear-cut and obvious and Mendel decided to study them individually. The fact that the flowers are normally self-pollinated was a great help to Mendel, for his flowers were not contaminated by unknown pollen. Mendel selected plants with opposed characters (e.g. tall and short) and bred them individually until he was satisfied that he had true-breeding lines, i.e. the tall plants produced only more tall ones. He then transferred pollen from tall plants to flowers of short ones and vice-versa. In both cases the next generation of plants (the *first filial* or F_1 generation) were all tall—the shortness characteristic of one parent had been suppressed, and Mendel stated that tallness is produced by some 'factor' in the cells which is *dominant* to a factor for shortness; the factor for shortness is said to be *recessive*. When the plants of the F_1 generation were allowed to set seed naturally (i.e. by self-fertilization), Mendel found that in every case he got about three times as many tall as short plants. Obviously the shortness factor was present in the F_1 plants and was passed on in the pollen or ovule to some of their offspring—the *second filial* or F_2 generation.

The constant appearance of the 3 : 1 ratio in the F_2 generation activated Mendel's mathematical mind and led him to what is now called *Mendel's First Law*. He suggested that the tallness and shortness factors, carried in the F_1 generation, separate during the formation of sex-cells

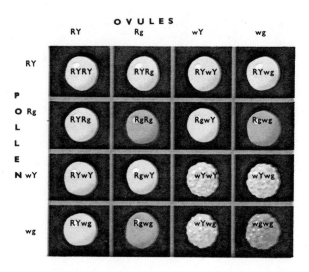

When round, yellow and wrinkled, green seeded plants are crossed, the F_1 generation produces four types of gamete which combine in every possible way, producing ine 9 : 3 : 3 : 1 ratio described in the text.

(*gametes*) so that half of the gametes carry the tallness factor and half carry the shortness factor.

Mendel's First Law states that *only one of two opposed characters can be carried as a factor in a single sex-cell, i.e. in a pollen grain or an ovule.*

If we accept this we can show how the 3 : 1 ratio is produced. Let the tallness factor be called T and the shortness factor, t. As Mendel started with true-breeding lines the original tall plants would produce gametes with only T, and the short ones only t. When these combine in the F_1 generation we have Tt. Because T is dominant all the plants are tall. According to Mendel's First Law, when these plants produce pollen and ovules there will be equal numbers of T and t gametes. Any pollen cell may fuse with any ovule when the pollen is released, and there are therefore four possible combinations in the F_2 generation as shown in the diagram. Three of these combinations

contain T and these plants are therefore tall while the remaining quarter are short. Two-thirds of the tall plants contain the shortness factor and, when self-pollinated, produce the 3 : 1, tall : short ratio. The other tall F_2 plants, however, are pure-breeding as are all the short ones—they have only one type of factor and are called *homozygotes*. The impure plants (i.e. those with two different factors) are *heterozygotes*.

Mendel then went on experimenting with peas which differed in two characters. He chose two types of plant—one with round, yellow seeds (RY), the other with wrinkled, green seeds (wg), and cross pollinated them. The resulting F_1 generation plants all had round, yellow seeds, so we can see that the factor for round seeds is dominant to that for wrinkled and that yellow dominates green. When the F_1 generation were self-fertilised the F_2 generation produced seed which showed all four characters in every possible combination. The proportions were very close to 9 round, yellow: 3 round, green: 3 wrinkled, yellow: 1 wrinkled, green. Mendel then enunciated what is now known as his second law:

The factor for *each one of a pair of opposed characters may combine with any one of another pair when the sex-cells are formed.* He reasoned that the impure F_1 plants would be RYwg and that they would produce the gametes RY, Rg, wY and wg. Rw and Yg cannot be produced because according to the first law a gamete can carry only one of a pair of opposed factors. Any pollen cell can again combine with any ovule and from the accompanying table we can see how Mendel explained the 9 : 3 : 3 : 1 ratio on this basis. Whenever R and

Y occur together there will be round yellow seeds, for these two factors are dominant. When R is absent they will be wrinkled, and when Y is absent they will be green.

When Mendel published his results in 1865 scientists paid little attention to his work.

The Role of Chromosomes

It was not until about 1900 (16 years after Mendel's death) that the validity of Mendel's work was realised. Several botanists, working independently, obtained similar results and confirmed Mendel's laws in many cases. There were, however, some exceptions. By now the techniques of microscopy were advancing and the chromosomes had been discovered. The chromosomes seemed the obvious site for Mendel's factors to be carried and we now know that this is so. The factors, which we call *genes*, are very complicated combinations of nucleic acids and nucleoproteins. The information is carried in the nucleic acid. A slight chemical change might convert a gene for tallness into one for shortness. Every gene occurs at a fixed point on a fixed chromosome. Since the chromosomes occur in pairs there will be in each cell two genes controlling height. These may both be tallness factors or both shortness factors (*homozygous* condition) or there may be one of each (*heterozygous* or impure condition). When sex-cells are formed the chromosomes undergo a process called *meiosis*. During meiosis the pairs of chromosomes separate – one of each pair going to each sex-cell (gamete). This is exactly what is proposed in Mendel's first law – only one of a pair of factors can occur in a single gamete. The gametes from a *homozy-*

gous individual will all be the same, but an impure individual will give two types in equal numbers.

Mendel was lucky in that the characters he chose – e.g. shape and colour of seeds – are borne on separate chromosomes. Had they been *linked genes* (i.e. on one chromosome) the results would have been different. He would have obtained only round, yellow seeds and wrinkled green

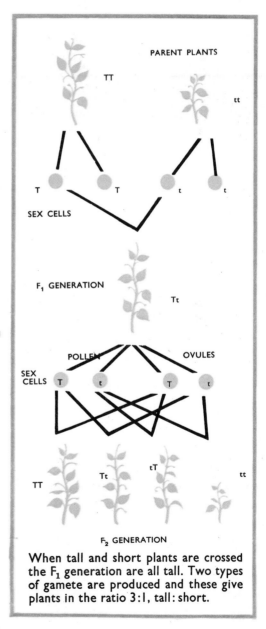

PARENT PLANTS

TT

tt

SEX CELLS

T   T   t   t

F₁ GENERATION

Tt

POLLEN   OVULES

SEX CELLS   T   t   T   t

F₂ GENERATION

TT   Tt   tT   tt

When tall and short plants are crossed the F₁ generation are all tall. Two types of gamete are produced and these give plants in the ratio 3:1, tall:short.

Gregor Mendel.

ones, for RY and wg would not have separated and Mendel would have been unable to make his second assumption. This does happen with many characters because of the enormous numbers of genes on each chromosome. Linkage causes a major exception to the second law. Linked genes can be separated, however, and often are by the occurrence of *crossing over*. The chromosomes may break and rejoin in different ways during meiosis so that various combinations are produced. This is an important source of variation in living things.

Linked Genes and Chromosome Maps

Mendel's work last century with garden peas led him to believe that every characteristic of an organism was controlled by a pair of 'factors' in each cell. He suggested that one 'factor' of each pair came from each parent. When sex-cells were produced the pairs of 'factors' split up and one went to each new cell. Microscopes were not very advanced in Mendel's day, however, and he was unable to show how the 'factors' could be passed on from one generation to the next. His work was forgotten for a considerable time.

During the 1880's, advances in microscopic technique made possible the discovery of the chromosomes – the thread-like bodies in the cell nucleus. Then, in 1900, Mendel's work was rediscovered. Walter Sutton, working in America, studied the behaviour of chromosomes during division of the cells and he realized that the process closely followed Mendel's theory for the behaviour of his 'factors'. Sutton put forward the 'chromosome theory of heredity' – that the 'factors' (or *genes* as they are now called) are carried on the chromosomes, one of each pair of genes on each member of a chromosome pair. This theory is now supported by a wealth of evidence.

Because there are a very large number of genes and only a relatively few chromosomes, each chromosome must carry many genes strung out along its length. Breeding experiments with various organisms – notably the fruit-fly *Drosophila* – have established a number of *linkage groups* – groups of characteristics that are normally inherited together because their genes are on the same chromosome. These linkage groups have enabled geneticists to 'map the chromosomes'.

New combinations occur occasionally even with linked genes. This can be explained only by assuming that the chromosomes break and rejoin in different ways during division. This is known as *crossing over* and has actually been observed under the microscope.

T. H. Morgan, another American scientist, suggested that the greater the distance between the two genes on a chromosome, the greater the chances of a break occurring between them. The amount of crossing over between two genes could therefore be used as an estimate of the relative distance between them on the chromosome. In an

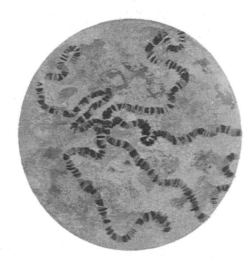

Giant chromosomes from the salivary glands of the fruit fly grub. Certain genes are now known to occur on certain bands of the chromosomes.

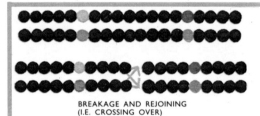

BREAKAGE AND REJOINING
(I.E. CROSSING OVER)

When linked genes appear in new combinations it must be assumed that the chromosomes have broken and rejoined in another way.

CHANCES OF A BREAK BETWEEN **D** AND **F**
ARE MUCH GREATER THAN BETWEEN **D** AND **E**

Morgan reasoned that the chances of a break between two given genes are greater if the genes are widely separated. He suggested that the rate of occurrence of a break between two genes (shown by the percentage of recombined characteristics in breeding experiments) could be used as a measure of the distance between them on the chromosome.

POSSIBLE POSITIONS OF **X**

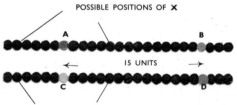

15 UNITS

POSSIBLE POSITIONS OF **Y**

Morgan and his associates worked with many pairs of linked genes to make their chromosome maps. This is a simplified example. Suppose the re-combinations AD and CB occur in 15% of the off-spring. A and B and C and D would then be placed fifteen units apart. Now take another pair of genes X and Y. The re-combinations AY and CX occur is say 5%, so X is 5 units from A. But there are two possible positions – one each side of A. Which is correct? Testing the crossing over between X and B will give the answer. If XB and YB occur in 10% then X is 10 units from B and lies between A and B. If XD and YB occur in 20%, then X lies on the far side of A. We thus have a simple map. Other genes can be placed by testing against these known fixed genes.

17

enormous number of experiments, Morgan studied cross-overs between a large number of genes in *Drosophila* and was able to produce detailed 'maps'.

Chromosome maps are now available for a number of other animals and plants, although not in such detail as the fruit-fly maps. *Drosophila* has only four pairs of chromosomes and many

Thomas Hunt Morgan with some varieties of Drosophila.

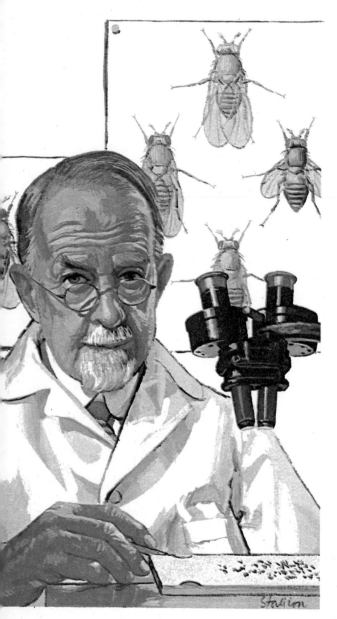

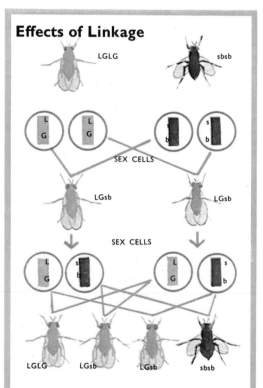

Effects of Linkage

In the fruit-fly, the genes for wing-length and body-colour are linked – i.e., they occur on the same chromosome. Only one pair of chromosomes is concerned in the transmission of these characteristics. The sex-cells of the original flies each carry a chromosome with either L and G genes or s and b genes.

Flies of the next generation contain two chromosomes concerned with wing length and body colour. One carries L and G genes and the other, s and b genes. When sex-cells are formed by this generation, the chromosome pairs separate so that each sex cell contains either L and G *or* s and b. These join with sex-cells from another fly in such a way that only long-winged grey and short-winged black flies appear in the next generation.

of the genes can be ascribed to their correct chromosome.

The linkage groups – corresponding in number to the pairs of chromosomes – are ascribed one to each pair of chromosomes and the map constructed. It is possible to do this without even seeing the chromosomes because the map is based only on the results of breeding experiments.

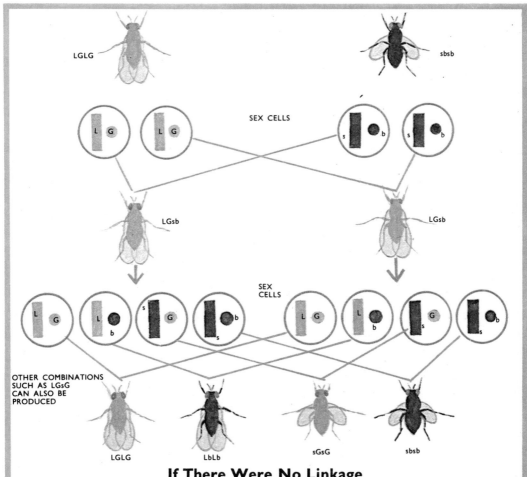

If There Were No Linkage

If the genes for body-colour and wing-length were not linked, two pairs of chromosomes would be involved – the pair carrying the colour genes and the pair carrying the wing-length genes.

In the original flies, the members of each pair of chromosomes are alike. When sex-cells are formed, one of each pair of chromosomes goes into each cell. The first generation of off-spring are hybrids but all have long wings and grey bodies because the genes for these dominate the black-body and short-winged genes. Each fly of this generation has the four genes L, G, s and b, all on separate chromosomes.

When this generation forms sex cells, each chromosome of a pair can go with either of the other pair. There are then four types of sex-cells. Any one of these can join with any of the four from another fly and so, allowing for dominance, there are four types of off-spring. The original long-winged grey and short-winged black flies have mingled their characteristics to produce long-winged black flies and short-winged grey ones.

The Reproduction of the Cell

The plant or animal body is made up of millions of cells, each finely constructed for a particular purpose. One may well ask what controls the structure of the cell; what ensures that each muscle fibre or plant cell is just like its neighbour and different from cells of another tissue?

We know that each cell in the body contains in its nucleus a fixed number of chromosomes. When cells divide a certain process ensures that the number of chromosomes remains constant. This process occurs in almost all living cells and is called *mitosis* (my-toe-sis).

For ease of description the process is divided into a number of stages although of course it is really continuous. A very generalized account is given in picture and caption form below.

Mitosis

The division of a cell and its nucleus is called *mitosis*. The chromosomes, which cannot be seen with an ordinary light microscope when the cell is not dividing, appear as double threads (1) soon after mitosis starts. The diagrams show what happens to four chromosomes, one red, one blue, one green and another orange, during mitosis. As mitosis proceeds they become arranged (2) on a network of strands – called the spindle – eventually lying around the equator of the spindle (3). The two threads of which each chromosome is made then pull apart (4) towards the opposite poles of the spindle so that four lie at one pole and four at the other (5). A membrane then forms around each set of four chromosomes and the cell becomes thinner (constricts) between each set (6). Eventually the constriction passes right across the cell and a new cell wall is formed resulting in the formation of two daughter cells each with four chromosomes in its nucleus.

When the cell is not in the process of dividing, the chromosomes in its nucleus are not clearly visible under the ordinary light microscope. The length of time required for mitosis varies from species to species but an average of six to twenty-four hours is a reasonable figure.

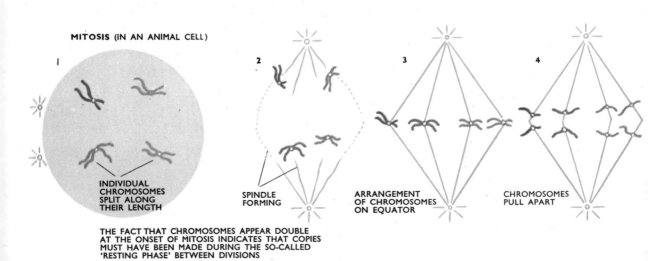

MITOSIS (IN AN ANIMAL CELL)

INDIVIDUAL CHROMOSOMES SPLIT ALONG THEIR LENGTH

SPINDLE FORMING

ARRANGEMENT OF CHROMOSOMES ON EQUATOR

CHROMOSOMES PULL APART

THE FACT THAT CHROMOSOMES APPEAR DOUBLE AT THE ONSET OF MITOSIS INDICATES THAT COPIES MUST HAVE BEEN MADE DURING THE SO-CALLED 'RESTING PHASE' BETWEEN DIVISIONS

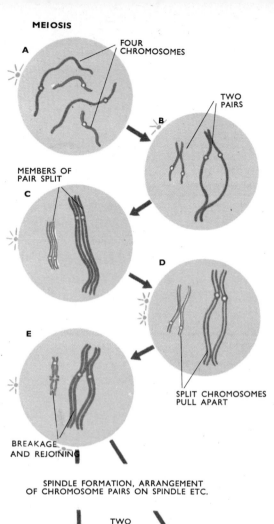

A — FOUR CHROMOSOMES

B — TWO PAIRS

MEMBERS OF PAIR SPLIT

C

D

SPLIT CHROMOSOMES PULL APART

E — BREAKAGE AND REJOINING

Meiosis

During the formation of sex cells the number of chromosomes is halved, so that each sex cell has half the number of chromosomes possessed by each of the body cells. When male and female sex cells join during fertilization, therefore, the full number of chromosomes is made up again. The process by which the chromosome number is halved is called *meiosis*.

During the early stages of mitosis (see diagrams) the chromosomes appear as double threads. This is not so in meiosis. The chromosomes are single threads (illustration A) (in these pictures the fate of four chromosomes is followed). They then come together in pairs (B) forming two pairs, the chromosomes of each pair lying closely together. Each chromosome then divides into two by splitting along its length (C). The pairs of double chromosomes become arranged on the equator of the spindle which has by this time formed. The split chromosomes then pull apart from each other but they remain attached at one or more points (D). The pairs of chromosomes then be-

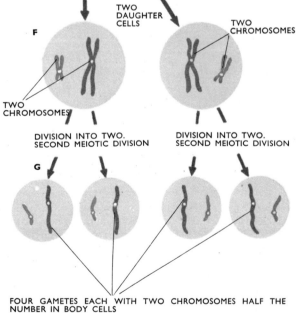

SPINDLE FORMATION, ARRANGEMENT OF CHROMOSOME PAIRS ON SPINDLE ETC.

F — TWO DAUGHTER CELLS — TWO CHROMOSOMES

TWO CHROMOSOMES

DIVISION INTO TWO. SECOND MEIOTIC DIVISION

DIVISION INTO TWO. SECOND MEIOTIC DIVISION

G

FOUR GAMETES EACH WITH TWO CHROMOSOMES HALF THE NUMBER IN BODY CELLS

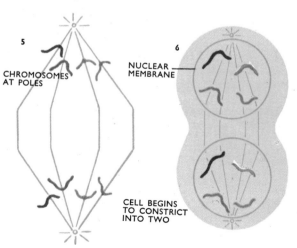

5 — CHROMOSOMES AT POLES

6 — NUCLEAR MEMBRANE

CELL BEGINS TO CONSTRICT INTO TWO

come arranged on a spindle much as in mitosis (stage 3), and the individual chromosomes move to the poles, each chromosome of each pair pulling away from the other. The net result is two daughter cells (F) each containing two split chromosomes – half the number (four) in the original cell. For this reason meiosis is often referred to as a reduction division. The number of chromosomes is reduced to half. Following the reduction part of meiosis is a second division (similar to mitosis) in which each of the daughter cells divides into two, forming a total of four sex cells or gametes, each containing two chromosomes.

Reduction of the Chromosome Number

The reproductive process in most plants and animals involves the joining of nuclei from the two parents. If each parent nucleus had a pair of each type of chromosome, the offspring's nuclei would have two pairs and so on. This state of affairs would soon become impossible and there is a special arrangement in almost all organisms whereby the chromosome number is halved at some stage of the reproductive process. This process is called *meiosis* (my-oh-sis). The normal body cells contain two of each type of chromosome – the *diploid* condition. The sex cells are formed from these by meiotic division and each then contains one set of chromosomes (the *haploid* condition). Like mitosis, meiosis can be divided into several stages (see illustrations and captions).

If we return to Mendel's experiments in which he crossed tall and short pea plants we can start to understand one of the most remarkable and exciting connections in the whole of biology. You will recall that hybrid plants from the cross were tall and that these tall plants when self-pollinated gave *both* tall and short plants in the ratio of 3 to 1. To explain this result Mendel invented a theory which used the idea that although a plant may contain instructions for tall and short, the pollen grains or ovules would contain one instruction only, either tall or short

During meiosis a cell containing say 12 chromosomes produces sex cells which contain 6 chromosomes (if you like, 2N and N respectively). Of the 6 pairs (12 individual chromosomes) only one member of each pair (6 individual chromosomes) gets into the sex cell.

The chromosomes have behaved in the same way as the instructions. This remarkable fact has led to the belief that the chromosomes carry the instructions. The chromosomes are thought to be a 'library of instructions', which are followed as the organism develops.

As a result of his work with garden peas, Gregor Mendel suggested a way in which characteristics could be passed on from one generation to the next. He suggested that the characteristics were inherited in the form of 'factors' which were carried in the sex-cells. From his discoveries he was able to put forward two laws which appeared to explain the control of inheritance.

We now know that some of Mendel's ideas were correct and we can explain them. What he called 'factors' are now called *genes*. They can be regarded as 'chemical messengers' which pass information from parents to off-spring. The genes occur on thread-like structures – the chromosomes. Each of the genes – for example, those controlling albinism in Man – occurs at a certain point on a certain chromosome. The cells of the body normally contain two *sets* of

chromosomes (or twenty-three pairs in Man) so that there will be two genes governing the presence or absence of this defect. If both are the same, i.e. both normal or both albino, the individual is *homozygous*, or pure, for the character. If there is one of each gene he is *heterozygous*, or hybrid for albinism.

When the sex-cells are formed, the pairs of chromosomes separate and one of each pair goes to each sex-cell. This is in agreement with Mendel's first law – only one of a pair of genes can be in a single sex-cell. Each one of a pair of chromosomes can go into a sex-cell with any one of another pair.

A great deal of genetical work has been done with the fruit-fly *Drosophila*. It has the advantages of a rapid life-cycle, large numbers of offspring, and it has also very large chromosomes in its salivary glands.

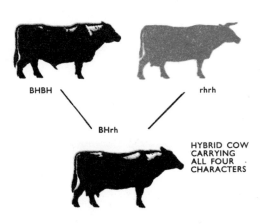

BHBH

rhrh

BHrh

HYBRID COW CARRYING ALL FOUR CHARACTERS

Because black coat and hornlessness are dominant all the offspring of this match will be black and have no horns.

SEX-CELLS

	BH	Bh	rH	rh
BH	BHBH	BHBh	BHrH	BHrh
Bh	BhBH	BhBh	BhrH	Bhrh
rH	rHBH	rHBh	rHrH	rHrh
rh	rhBH	rhBh	rhrH	rhrh

When two hybrid black hornless cattle are crossed, four types of off-spring will result. Wherever B occurs the animal will be black. Where H occurs there will be no horns.

23

By studying these for many generations of flies it has been possible to 'map' them, showing where different genes occur in them.

Mendel's laws can be used to explain and even predict the characteristics of offspring of given parents, provided that the characteristics are due to the action of a gene or genes. It is important to distinguish between *genetic effects* and *environmental effects* caused by differences in diet, upbringing, etc.

Most human traits, such as hair colour, are produced by the action of several genes. However, it has been discovered that the ability to taste a chemical, phenylthiocarbonate (P.T.C.), is inherited as a simple

Mendelian dominant, just like round seed shape in peas. The ability to taste P.T.C. is incidental to our ordinary sense of taste and it cannot be acquired through training. Either you can taste it or you can't! The way in which the ability to taste P.T.C. is inherited is shown in the illustrations.

Black coat dominates red coat in cattle. A cross between red and black animals will produce nothing but hybrid black offspring in the first generation. If these hybrid black ones are crossed, about a quarter of the next generation will be red, half will be hybrid black and a quarter will be pure black. The 3:1 ratio of black to red is called the *mono-hybrid*

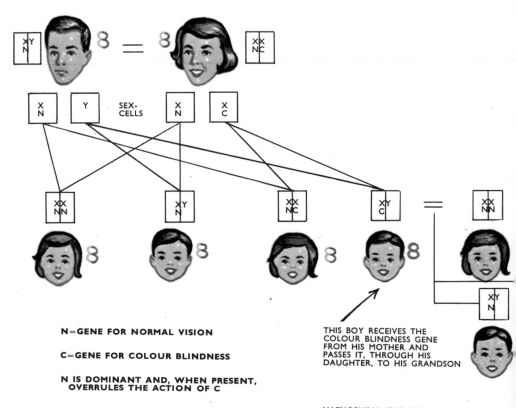

N=GENE FOR NORMAL VISION

C=GENE FOR COLOUR BLINDNESS

N IS DOMINANT AND, WHEN PRESENT, OVERRULES THE ACTION OF C

THIS BOY RECEIVES THE COLOUR BLINDNESS GENE FROM HIS MOTHER AND PASSES IT, THROUGH HIS DAUGHTER, TO HIS GRANDSON

HAEMOPHILIA, THE DISEASE IN WHICH THE BLOOD CANNOT CLOT, IS TRANSMITTED IN THE SAME WAY AS COLOUR BLINDNESS

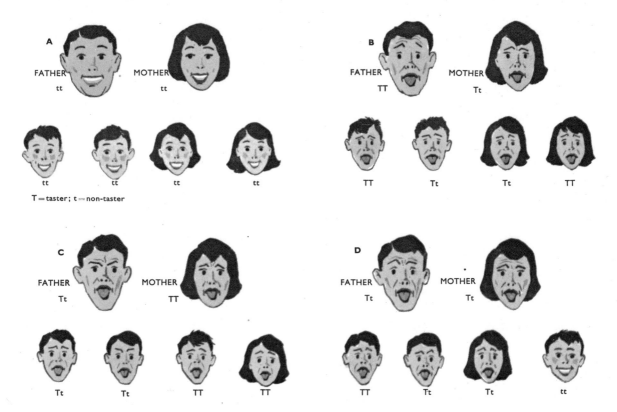

The ability to taste phenylthiocarbonate is dominant to the inability to taste phenylthio-carbonate so that (A) when both father and mother are non-tasters (tt) all the children are non-tasters (tt). If one parent is TT and the other Tt (B and C) then all the children will be tasters (TT or Tt). If both parents are Tt (D), however, then they may have a non-tasting child (tt).

Red green colour-blindness is sex-linked. Affected persons cannot distinguish red and green so that the two-colour figure '8' will appear to them as one colour only.

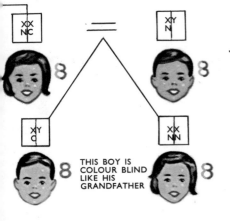

THIS BOY IS COLOUR BLIND LIKE HIS GRANDFATHER

ratio because only one pair of characteristics is being studied.

Hornlessness in cattle is dominant to the horned condition and a cross between a pure black hornless animal (e.g. an Aberdeen Angus) and a red, horned one will result in hybrid black, hornless first generation offspring. Because any one of a pair of characteristics can combine with any one of another pair, the second generation will show four types in the proportion, black hornless 9: black horned 3: red hornless 3: red horned 1. This ratio is called the *di-hybrid ratio*. When three, four or even more characters are considered a fixed proportion is still obtained.

Male or Female?

Many animals and the majority of plants are *hermaphrodite* – i.e. they have both male and female sex organs. In those where the sexes are separate, a genetic mechanism normally decides whether an individual may be male or female. Although it is usually stated that Man has 23 pairs of chromosomes, there are, in the male, only 22 *pairs*, plus two odd ones called the *sex-chromosomes* or the X and Y *chromosomes*. The female has two X chromosomes, making 23 true pairs. When the sex-cells are formed the pairs separate so that each female cell (egg) has an X chromosome. Half the male cells will contain a Y chromosome and the other half an X. If a male cell containing an X chromosome fuses with an egg-cell a female will develop, whereas a male cell containing Y will produce a male embryo. Because the X and Y are present in equal numbers boys and girls will be produced in nearly equal numbers too. The female is not the XX sex in all animals. In birds the hen is XY while the male is XX.

Sex-linked Genes

The Y chromosome in Man rarely carries genes which are not concerned with sex, but the X chromosome, which is larger, does carry some other genes. The characteristics that these produce are said to be *sex-linked*. Red/green colour-blindness, in which the sufferer cannot distinguish between red and green, is an example. The gene is recessive to that for normal vision so that, except in the very rare cases in which two colour-blindness genes occur together, women do not suffer from this defect. They do, however, act as carriers and may pass the gene to their offspring. If a male receives this recessive gene he will be colour-blind because there is no normal vision gene on the Y chromosome. The colour-blindness is thus transmitted through the female. A man cannot pass the defect on to his son because only the Y chromosome goes to the son.

Male or Female?

The female has two X chromosomes, the male has one X and one Y sex-chromosome. When the sex-cells are formed the pairs separate, so that each female cell (egg) must contain an X chromosome, but half the male cells will contain an X chromosome and half a Y. A male X cell fusing with a female cell (XX) will develop as a female, whereas a male Y will produce (XY) a male.

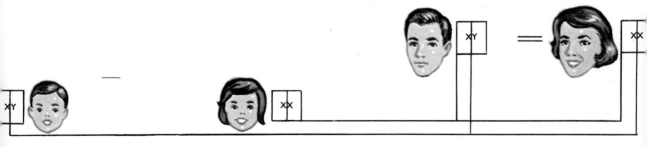

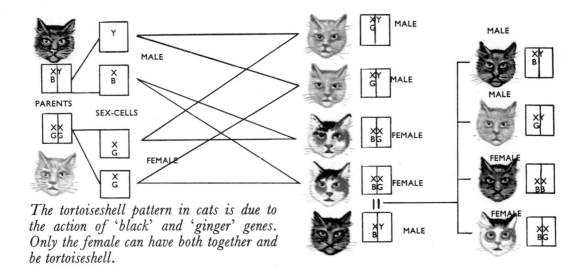

The tortoiseshell pattern in cats is due to the action of 'black' and 'ginger' genes. Only the female can have both together and be tortoiseshell.

Sex Linkage in Cats

The *tortoiseshell* characteristic in cats is found only in the female. The genes for black or ginger coats are carried on the *X* chromosome. There is incomplete dominance and the two genes together produce a tortoiseshell. As only the female has two *X* chromosomes only she can show this characteristic. Males are either black or ginger because they have only one *X* chromosome and therefore can carry only the black-coat gene *or* the ginger-coat gene.

THEORIES ABOUT THE WAY IN WHICH CHROMOSOMES WORK

A difference of one chromosome makes all the difference between maleness and femaleness in beetles. In mammals, the absence of one piece of a chromosome has the same effect as the absence of a complete chromosome in beetles. Each species of animal and plant has its characteristic number and pattern of chromosomes. This is just some of the evidence that supports the idea that chromosomes decide that one fertilized egg will develop into one kind of organism, another fertilized egg into another. It is reasonable to think of chromosomes as *instructions* which the developing plant or animal follows. But there are difficult problems in understanding how these instructions work.

Some pine trees have 24 chromosomes in each nucleus, so do the cells of some salamanders. It would be reasonable to guess that the chromosomes of pine trees must be of a very different chemical make-up from those of salamanders.

Chemists have successfully investigated the chemical nature of chromosomes, having first separated them from cells. It seems that no matter which organism, plant or animal, is used as the source of chromosomes, the chemical nature of the chromosomes is very similar. Now how can 24 chromosomes which are chemically very similar cause one egg to become a pine tree and another to become a salamander?

Further information supplied by

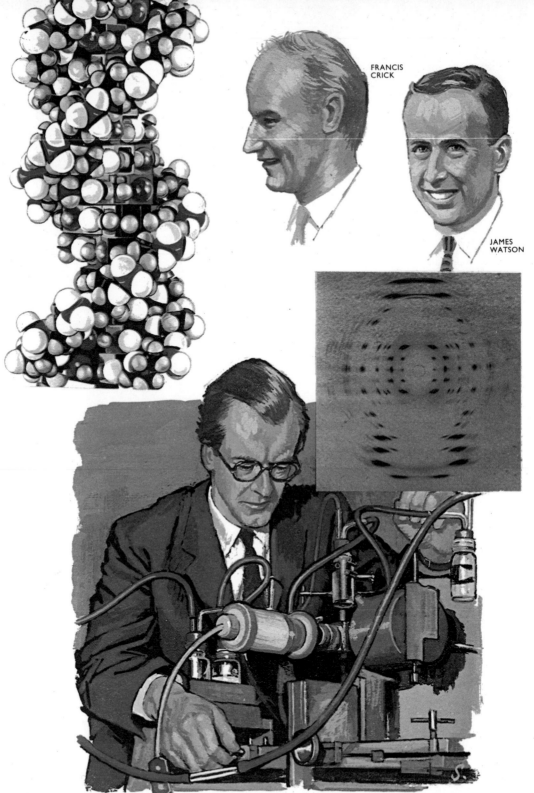

FRANCIS CRICK

JAMES WATSON

Prof. Maurice Wilkins using X-ray diffraction apparatus. Samples subjected to this treatment scatter the X-rays and produce patterns such as that above. The arrangement of the dark areas depends upon the arrangement of the molecules and their constituent atoms in the sample. From such data, Crick and Watson (above right) built up their model of DNA (above left), for which work they all three received the Nobel prize.

28

chemical analysis was that chromosomes contain chemically-linked sugar molecules, phosphate groups and almost always four other substances (which will be referred to by their initial letters, A, T, C, and G) – linked to form a long chain molecule. A, T, C, and G are collectively called *bases*.

The sugar and phosphate content of the chromosomes from different organisms is the same weight for weight.

The main difference found between chromosome analyses are in the amounts of A, T, C, and G. This is not a very promising start in a search for an explanation of the difference between all the different species of living organisms.

An important additional bit of information supplied by the analyst was that in any given chromosome there is an equal amount of A and T. The amounts of substances C and G are also the same but the amounts of A + T and C + G vary from one species to another. It was already known that, because of their chemical structure, A and T would fit together easily, as would C and G; but combinations A–G; A–C; T–G; T–C were much less likely to occur. This information, scant though it is, was the foundation on which important theories were laid.

The information was first used to solve a simple problem – simple that is compared to how chromosomes work – how do chromosomes reproduce themselves?

Chromosome Replication

As a result of cell division, each new cell contains a complete set of chromosomes just like those in the parent cell. Chromosomes must be able to make exact copies of themselves. This remarkable property is at the very root of life. The molecules usually studied by chemists may combine to form larger molecules or chains, but the idea of a molecule being able to take material from its surroundings and duplicate itself is very remarkable indeed.

Francis Crick and James Watson, two scientists working at Cambridge, collected all the information they could on the analysis of chromosome material and in 1953 they produced a model of the 'chromosome molecule' or DNA. They suggested that DNA consisted of two chains of alternate sugar and phosphate molecules with one of the bases, A, T, C or G, attached to each sugar group. They proposed that an A base in one chain joined with a T base in the other chain, and the same for C and G. If we represent the sugar + phosphate groups by ◣ the DNA molecule would look like diagram A on Page 30.

In fact, all the evidence suggests that the chains coil around each other so that Crick and Watson's model was more like a spiral staircase (Diagram B) than the plain ladder.

Now imagine that this long ladder-like molecule exists in a 'soup' containing sugar and phosphate groups linked to A, T, C, or G groups. These linked groups are called *nucleotides*. Such a 'soup' might well be found in the nucleus of a cell. Suppose now that the chains uncoiled and the 'rungs' of the ladder – the A + T groups and the C + G groups – divided. The nucleotides could join on to these broken 'rungs'. Because of their special properties, A would join on only where there was previously an A, C would join on only where there was previously a C, and so on (see diagram C on page 31).

We can see that there would now be two double chains where there was previously only one. More important, the new chains would be identical with the old one because the A, T, C, and G groups linked up in exactly the same way. The 'chromosome molecule' is thus able to reproduce itself exactly as long as it is supplied with 'food' – that is to say, a supply of A, T, C, and G groups, sugar and phosphate molecules, and energy required for the linking process.

Instructions for Development

The only way in which the chromosomes could possibly carry information which might cause one egg to become a human and another to become a dog is in the form of a

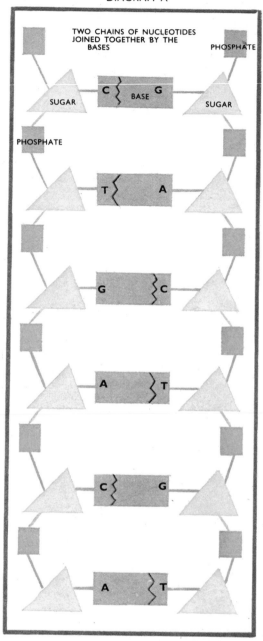

TWO CHAINS OF NUCLEOTIDES JOINED TOGETHER BY THE BASES

PHOSPHATE

SUGAR

C { BASE G

SUGAR

PHOSPHATE

T { A

G { C

A { T

C { G

A { T

The nucleotides join together to form a sort of twisted 'ladder' in which the sugar and phosphate groups form the uprights and the bases, the rungs.

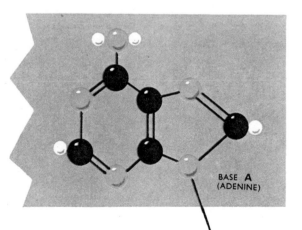

BASE **A**
(ADENINE)

Adenine nucleotide – one of the 'building blocks' of nucleic acids. Each nucleotide consists of a sugar molecule, a phosphate group and a 'base'.

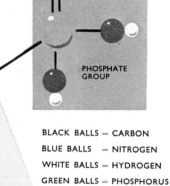

PHOSPHATE GROUP

SUGAR MOLECULE

BLACK BALLS = CARBON
BLUE BALLS = NITROGEN
WHITE BALLS = HYDROGEN
GREEN BALLS = PHOSPHORUS

DIAGRAM B

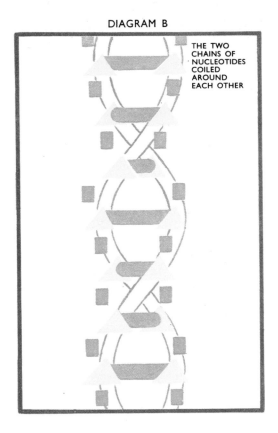

THE TWO CHAINS OF NUCLEOTIDES COILED AROUND EACH OTHER

REPLICATION OF DNA

When all the 'rungs' have been completed by new 'building blocks' (nucleotides) there will be two new double chains. For simplicity, the chains are shown completely separated instead of coiled.

DIAGRAM C

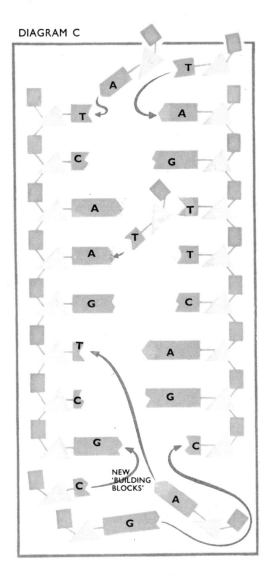

NEW 'BUILDING BLOCKS'

CODE. The Morse code used in telegraphy is made up of two units – a dot and a dash – and a particular sequence of dots and/or dashes indicates a particular letter or number. By arranging the dots and dashes in the right order whole books full of information can be put into code.

The 'rungs' of the 'chromosome molecule' are composed of A + T groups, T + A groups, C + G groups or G + C groups. Any one of these can follow any other and so there are many ways of arranging them. It is believed that different arrangements of the 'rungs' represent different instructions, just as different arrangements of the dots and dashes represent different words.

The Difference Between Species

While we normally recognise differences between species or varieties of plants and animals by their structure, such as number of legs, or shape of leaves, there are other differences we could use to separate groups, or even individuals. We could use chemical means, for example, petal colours in flowers, or blood groups in mammals and birds. It is even possible to distinguish by chemical analysis between sea urchin eggs of different species which are otherwise indistinguishable at early stages of their development.

That part of the weight of living things which is not water or skeletal material is mainly protein. Each species has its own particular proteins, many proteins may be similar but a few are unique to a species. We could, if we knew enough about the chemistry of protoplasm, describe and classify species by the proteins they contain. Indeed, work in this field has thrown up some very interesting evidence of value in the study of evolution. For instance, there is strong evidence for presuming that the gorilla and the chimpanzee are more closely related to Man than they are to the orang-utan and the gibbon. On this basis the gorilla and the chimpanzee might well be included in the same family as Man – the Hominidae. Similarly, whales are more closely related to the even-toed ungulates than they are to any other mammals. Four flightless birds studied all come from the same evolutionary stock – the rhea, cassowary, emu and ostrich.

Now it may be that a species develops in a particular way characteristic for that species because it produces proteins characteristic of that species. But how is it decided which kind of proteins will be made by the egg protoplasm?

Proteins vary from soluble powders, such as casein, to tough fibres such as keratin. All proteins appear to be **made up of chains, each link of which is an amino acid.**

Proteins differ because the types of amino acids they contain are different, or because they contain different proportions of the same amino acids, or because they contain the acids joined in a different sequence.

The way in which cells grow depends on the way the protoplasm grows, which depends on the proteins which are formed, which depends on the way the amino acids are strung together. Imagine a protein from a cow (very much simplified)

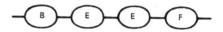

consisting of three amino acids B, E, and F, one of which is represented twice in the protein molecule. A protein from a sheep might be:

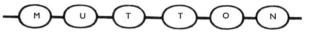

The proteins differ because the amino acids they contain are different.

The problem is, what decided that in the developing cow's egg the amino acids B, E, E, F were pieced together in this particular order to form a chain but not other amino acids which must have been available? After all, both cows and sheep eat grass.

Up to now we have thought that the chromosomes in, say, a cow's egg decided that the egg would become a cow. Is there any connection between the chromosomes and the manufacture of protein? If we knew where the proteins were made in cells a useful start would be made on this problem. This has been investigated by mincing liver cells and centrifuging (spinning) the mince to separate the nuclei from the rest (the cytoplasm) and 'feeding' the separate fractions with radio-active amino acids. Any proteins are then recovered, and if the proteins are radioactive we can say that the radioactive amino acids have been joined up to form the radioactive proteins.

The results of this investigation showed that the nucleus does not make protein, but the cytoplasm does. We can only conclude that there does not appear to be a *direct* connection between protein manufacture and 'chromosome molecules'. Fortunately, the story does not end here. The nucleus contains what we call 'chromosome molecules', made up of chains of sugar, phosphate, and A, T, C and G. Now cells also contain a similar substance called RNA which also contains sugar and phosphate units and three of the four substances A, T, C, G. Of the total amount of this substance present in the cell usually $\frac{9}{10}$ occurs in the cytoplasm, $\frac{1}{10}$ in the nucleus.

There is evidence (from the use of radioactive tracers) that the RNA is made in the nucleus and then transferred to the cytoplasm.

Now if the RNA is made on the surface of a 'chromosome molecule' the RNA might be able to copy *part* of the 'chromosome molecule'. RNA molecules are known to be smaller than 'chromosome molecules' and unlike the latter can get out of the nucleus. The RNA molecules may be *messengers* carrying instructions from the 'chromosome molecules' to the cytoplasm where the protein is made, carrying messages in a code written in chemical language which decides the order in which amino acids in the cell are to be linked together to make proteins.

The vitally important question which remains is, how do the amino acids 'know' which position to take on the messenger RNA? Or if you compare the code with Morse code,

how is the translation from code to amino acid language done? If the signal ... – – – ... is to mean anything to us, we must know that ... is S and – – – is O. We need to have connected in our minds the sounds dot, dot, dot, with the letter S. Similarly, in the cell there needs to be some connection between code units and letters of the protein language, that is amino acids. If such a connection could not be found this elaborate theory would have to be discarded. Such 'translator units' have been found. It has been shown that in the cytoplasm small RNA units with small groups of code molecules A, C, G, are attached to particular amino acids. We may picture these units as follows:

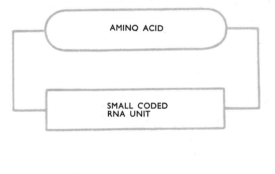

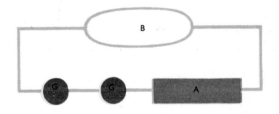

and visualise the theory of protein manufacture as in the diagrams on pages 34 and 35.

This theory fits a large number of known facts discovered about chromosomes and the manufacture of

A PICTORIAL REPRESENTATION OF THE THEORY CONNECTING CHROMOSOMES WITH PROTEIN MANUFACTURE

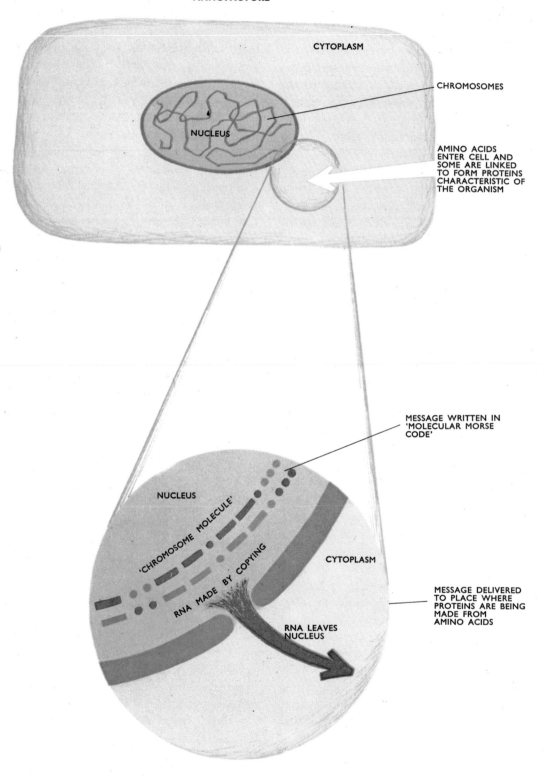

CYTOPLASM

CHROMOSOMES

NUCLEUS

AMINO ACIDS ENTER CELL AND SOME ARE LINKED TO FORM PROTEINS CHARACTERISTIC OF THE ORGANISM

MESSAGE WRITTEN IN 'MOLECULAR MORSE CODE'

NUCLEUS

'CHROMOSOME MOLECULE'

RNA MADE BY COPYING

CYTOPLASM

MESSAGE DELIVERED TO PLACE WHERE PROTEINS ARE BEING MADE FROM AMINO ACIDS

RNA LEAVES NUCLEUS

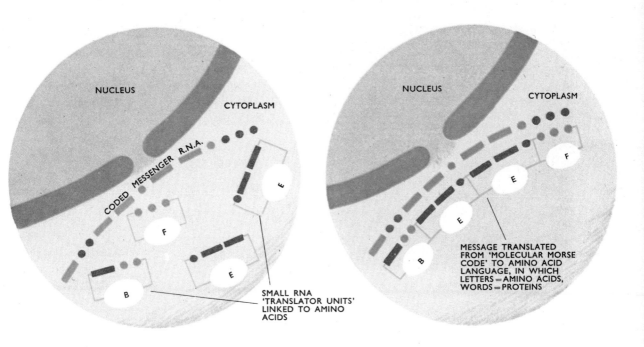

NUCLEUS CYTOPLASM

CODED MESSENGER R.N.A.

SMALL RNA 'TRANSLATOR UNITS' LINKED TO AMINO ACIDS

NUCLEUS CYTOPLASM

MESSAGE TRANSLATED FROM 'MOLECULAR MORSE CODE' TO AMINO ACID LANGUAGE, IN WHICH LETTERS = AMINO ACIDS, WORDS = PROTEINS

NUCLEUS CYTOPLASM

FREE MESSENGER RNA AVAILABLE TO REPEAT PROCESS

MANUFACTURED PROTEIN

FREE 'TRANSLATOR UNITS' AVAILABLE FOR PICKING UP MORE AMINO ACIDS—OF THE RIGHT KIND

proteins in cells, but this does not necessarily make it fact, it may be a fairy tale. After all we invent theories because they fit facts. How then can we test the theory?

If a theory is any good we can use it to make predictions. We can say that if something is done to the cell then certain things must follow if the theory is true. This is exactly what is happening to this theory now. One splendid experiment done recently depended on the ingenious idea that if you were able to feed into the protein manufacturing process small RNA units the same as those in the cell *but with a different amino acid attached* a protein perhaps very unusual for the species might be formed.

For example, if it were possible in our imaginary cow cell to feed in L

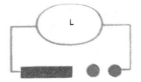

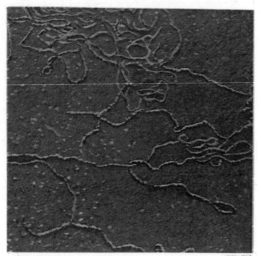

An electron micrograph of DNA strands.

units a protein L-E-E-F instead of B-E-E-F would be made, on some of the messenger RNA. This turned out to be a correct prediction, and gives us confidence that the theory may be true.

In the main text, the substances forming the 'rungs' of the 'chromosome molecules' have been called A, T, C and G. Their full names are adenine, thymine, cytosine, and guanine and their chemical structures are shown here. They are called bases for convenience. The big picture on page 30 shows how a base is linked to a sugar molecule and a phosphate group to form a nucleotide or 'half-rung'.

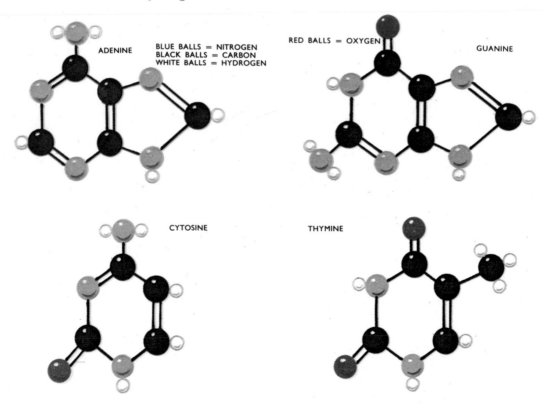

ADENINE

BLUE BALLS = NITROGEN
BLACK BALLS = CARBON
WHITE BALLS = HYDROGEN

RED BALLS = OXYGEN

GUANINE

CYTOSINE

THYMINE

The Evolutionary
Theory

CHAPTER THREE

What is a Species?

LIFE is present in numerous different forms. This becomes obvious from a glance around the countryside. An elm tree is very different from a holly tree; a rabbit is different from a jack-daw.

In the seventeenth century Carolus Linnaeus, the Swedish naturalist, attempted a complete classification of all the known living organisms of his day. By careful inspection and study he recognized a large number of different *species*. Each species consisted of individuals which were very alike in appearance. These interbred and the offspring produced were very similar to the parents. Thus all rabbits belong to one species and all polar bears to another.

Today we know that all the structures of organisms are genetically controlled – that is they depend upon the influence of small structures called genes which are present in the chromosomes of living cells. Members of one of Linnaeus's species are all alike in appearance because the structure and arrangement of genes on the chromosomes is similar. Each species keeps its own identity because the genes on its chromosomes will not successfully combine with the genes on the chromosomes of another species.

Thus instead of defining a species in terms of its appearance, it can now be defined in terms of genetics. A species is a group whose members will, in the wild, interbreed among themselves but will not successfully breed with members of another group.

Evolution and the Species

Linnaeus was a *Creationist*. He considered that all his different groups of individuals (species) were not only separate from one another now, but had always been separate from one another. All species had been created at the same time and none of them had changed since.

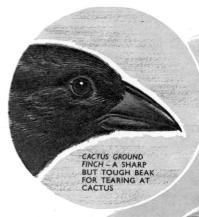

CACTUS GROUND FINCH – A SHARP BUT TOUGH BEAK FOR TEARING AT CACTUS

LARGE GROUND FINCH – BEAK IS ADAPTED FOR A DIET OF NUTS

Darwin discovered a dozen or so species of finch inhabiting the Galapagos Isles of the Pacific Ocean. The ancestral species of finch is believed to have come from South America 600 miles to the east. In different parts of the Archipelago new distinct species evolved from this original type, each adapted to a particular form of feeding.

The theory of Evolution put forward in 1859 by Wallace and Darwin explained things differently. According to the evolutionary theory more complicated organisms evolve gradually from simpler kinds. At some stage therefore one species must evolve into another. How does this take place? Certainly not directly. When two members of the same species interbreed they produce offspring very similar to themselves – not an individual belonging to an entirely new species. When dogs breed they always produce puppies and not kittens. Nor do members of different species cross-breed to produce a third species; except for very rare instances, species are incapable of successful interbreeding. A cat cannot breed with a dog to produce something mid-way between the two.

Instead, the process takes place over a very long time. Members of the same species may become separated by geographical barriers – rivers, mountains, seas. Two distinct populations or more are set up, each population, by natural selection, becoming adapted to the slightly different conditions in

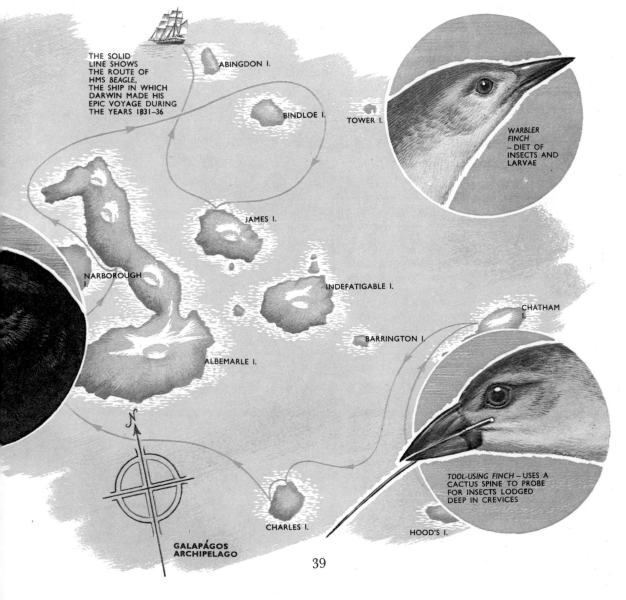

THE SOLID LINE SHOWS THE ROUTE OF HMS *BEAGLE*, THE SHIP IN WHICH DARWIN MADE HIS EPIC VOYAGE DURING THE YEARS 1831–36

ABINGDON I.

BINDLOE I.

TOWER I.

WARBLER FINCH – DIET OF INSECTS AND LARVAE

JAMES I.

NARBOROUGH I.

INDEFATIGABLE I.

CHATHAM I.

BARRINGTON I.

ALBEMARLE I.

N

TOOL-USING FINCH – USES A CACTUS SPINE TO PROBE FOR INSECTS LODGED DEEP IN CREVICES

CHARLES I.

HOOD'S I.

GALAPÁGOS ARCHIPELAGO

Separation between the horse and donkey is not quite complete. Members of the two groups are still able to interbreed but the offspring, a mule or a hinny, are sterile. Horses and donkeys can also cross with zebras; again the hybrids are sterile.

its own area. In this way *races* are formed. One race is slightly different from another, though members of different races can still interbreed and produce offspring. Man – the species *Homo sapiens* – illustrates race formation very well. All over the world are populations of men which have their own distinctive features – Negroes, Bushmen, Mongols, and so on.

The longer a race remains separated from other races of the same species, the more it is likely to diverge in appearance and in its genetical make-up. Finally a stage is reached when the race becomes so divergent with the other races that it can no longer interbreed with them. It is then a new species.

Between race and species there may be a very narrow borderline. A situation may be reached when a degree of interbreeding is still possible between members of two populations. Total isolation, where the two populations are incapable of interbreeding, is not quite reached. The offspring however are usually themselves sterile or they have inherent weaknesses which prevent them from surviving. An example is the horse and the donkey. Though these two animals are obviously separate forms, they can still interbreed. The offspring, a mule, cannot itself reproduce – it is sterile.

Such borderline cases are not uncommon and though they are troublesome in exactly separating a species from a race, they nevertheless provide valuable evidence that the process of evolution is working. They mark stages in the formation of a species, which have not quite been completed.

Linnaeus noticed that some species were very like others and could be distinguished only by some small structural differences. He therefore classified like species into larger groups called *genera*. Each individual in his classification then had two names. The generic name was written in latin with a capital first letter, followed by the specific name, also in latin, but with a small first letter. The meadow buttercup is thus called *Ranunculus acris*. The specific name is *acris* while the generic name is *Ranunculus* – a name shared by similar flowers such as the creeping buttercup *Ranunculus repens*.

Linnaeus's system of naming living organisms is still the scientific method used today. The explanation why some species are so like one another is that they are closely related – one has evolved from another or they have a common ancestor.

CHAPTER FOUR

The Case for Evolution

THE idea that living things have evolved (i.e. the more complex have developed from the simpler ones) is quite ancient and was first put forward by the early Greek philosophers. It has, however, always been opposed to a greater or lesser extent by the supporters of the theory of *special creation*. These people held that the many kinds of animals and plants were created by some super-natural force and have continued without alteration. Cuvier, the famous French biologist, (1769–1832) examined numerous fossils and found that most of them were of types no longer living. This led him to the theory of *Catastrophism* in which he stated that there had been several special creations throughout the Earth's history and that each had been wiped out by some further catastrophe. The theories of

special creation still have their supporters but have now been discarded by the scientific world. Evidence collected from various branches of biology has been put together to form what is known as the *general theory of evolution*. The evidence is not indisputable but the theory is the one that best fits the available facts.

In order to accept the idea of evolution we must first assume that living organisms originated from non-living matter a long way back in time. Exactly how this may have happened is one of the problems of biology. Acceptance of the idea of evolution also implies that life arose only once and that all forms come from this one spontaneous generation. This of course, cannot be proved, but Pasteur showed that bacteria cannot be created other than from bacteria already present. It

A possible evolutionary tree of the invertebrates. Most of the connections are merely theoretical.

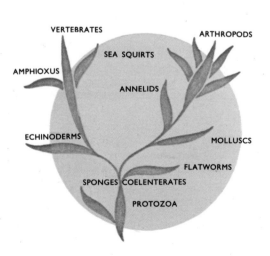

Evidence that molluscs and annelid worms had a common ancestor is provided by the existence of similar larval forms in some species.

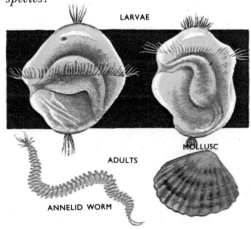

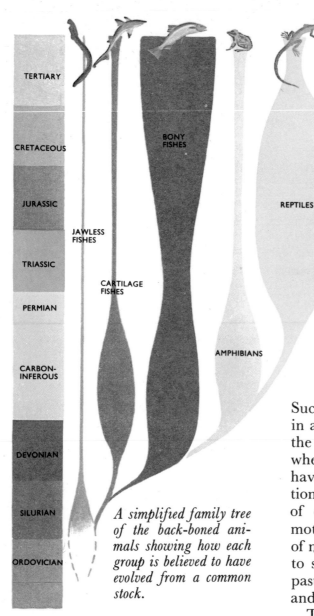

TERTIARY

CRETACEOUS

JURASSIC

TRIASSIC

PERMIAN

CARBON-
INFEROUS

DEVONIAN

SILURIAN

ORDOVICIAN

JAWLESS
FISHES

CARTILAGE
FISHES

BONY
FISHES

AMPHIBIANS

REPTILES

BIRDS

MAMMALS

A simplified family tree of the back-boned animals showing how each group is believed to have evolved from a common stock.

is possible, however, that smaller units of life – more akin to viruses – may have been produced more than once. If we assume that life originated only once we must also assume that all plants and animals are related and that the simpler forms give rise, along different lines, to the higher ones. This is the basis of the general theory of evolution.

Evolution implies the gradual change of one species into another.

Such changes have now been observed in a few cases. This is especially so in the case of domestic and farm animals where new and improved varieties have been produced by artificial selection. The almost sudden appearance of dark (*melanic*) forms of various moths in recent years is a good example of natural change. There is no reason to suppose that such changes in the past could not have given rise to new and distinct species in time.

The aim of classification is to group those animals that have a number of characteristics in common. The largest group is the *phylum* and its members all have a basic similarity. It is reasonable therefore to assume that the members all arose from a common ancestral type. The phyla themselves can be placed in some sort of order from the most simple to the most complicated but there are large gaps in the arrangement of present-day forms. These gaps may be filled when more fossils are known but, at present, we cannot say for certain whether star-fishes and insects had a common origin or whether they have evolved from independent beginnings.

Animal structure, too, provides evidence of evolution. The fins of a lungfish, the wings of a bird and the forelimbs of a dog are superficially very different but all arise from a similar part of the embryo: they are *homologous* structures. Internally, the basic bone patterns can be seen, too. These limbs therefore represent modifications of a basic type and point to evolution from a common ancestor.

In the nineteenth century, the *Recapitulation theory* was put forward. This suggested that, during development, an animal passed through stages resembling those of its evolutionary history and it was presented as support for evolution. The embryos do pass through various grades of development but cannot be said to resemble first a protozoan, then a coelenterate, and so on as the early supporters of the theory believed. The similarity between early vertebrate embryos is very striking and this, together with other evidence makes it quite clear that these animals originated from a common stock. An interesting similarity *between* different phyla is the existence of a particular type of larva in both molluscs and annelid (ringed) worms. This larval type is called the *trochophore* or *veliger*. It is possible that molluscs and worms originated from a common ancestor which had a larva of this type.

The greatest volume of evidence for evolution is provided by fossils, but here again the emphasis is on evolution within the major groups. The fossil record is very incomplete and almost non-existent before Cambrian times. At the beginning of this latter period, most of the major groups were in existence and we have no proof that the lower forms gave rise to the more advanced groups. Within the phyla, however, fossils show very clearly the evolution of new species. In successive rock layers the fossils become pro-

The basic similarity between the limbs of a lung fish, bird and man indicate a common origin. This sort of evidence strongly supports the theory of evolution.

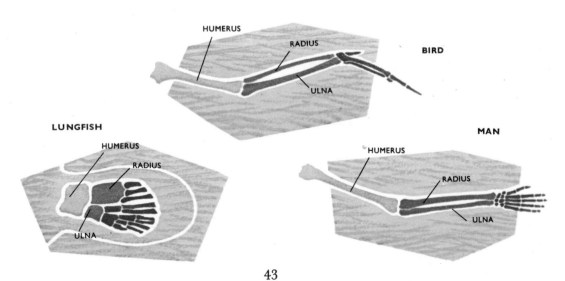

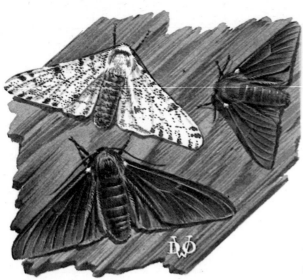

The increase and spread of the dark form of the peppered moth is a change that has actually been witnessed in recent years. The two varieties may eventually become separate species.

gressively more and more different until a new specific name is warranted. The vertebrates show a fuller fossil record than most of the invertebrates, for these animals with hard skeletons are well suited for preservation as fossils. Within the vertebrate group – as with the other phyla – the generalised forms gave rise to the more specialised and advanced ones. For example, the fishes arose from primitive jawless creatures and radiated into several branches. One of these gave rise to the amphibians which themselves evolved along several lines.

The geographical distribution of animals is another feature supporting the theory of evolution. In fact, it was by studying this that Darwin hit upon his theory of Natural Selection. Where any region, notably an island, has been separated from neighbouring parts, its animals, although super-ficially resembling those of the mainland, often differ in detail. The changes can be explained most easily by the fact that evolution has taken place. Australasia's native mammals are all egg-laying or pouched creatures. Presumably this whole region was separated before the placental mammals arose and in this region evolution did not follow along the line to the placentals.

Darwin visited the Galapagos Islands in 1835 and was struck by the variation among the birds and other animals. Although the islands are not very far apart, each has a distinct assemblage of bird species. This could be explained only on the basis of change since the birds first arrived, for it was highly improbable that one species arrived on only one island. Being isolated on each island, the birds were free to evolve in different directions and produce several different species. Darwin realised that this was the case and sought to find a method whereby this could have happened. He sought for it for a long time and many years later published his theory of Natural Selection.

We thus have a wealth of evidence to support a general theory of evolution. There is no direct evidence that life was created only once or that the various major groups are related, although similarities, such as that between young annelids and young molluscs, suggest that this might be so. There is direct evidence for the evolution within a group from simple to advanced forms and it is therefore possible that such evolution has taken place between the groups too. Until further fossils are found we cannot be sure but the evidence available supports on the whole the general theory of evolution.

CHAPTER FIVE

How Evolution Works

IF one accepts the idea that living things evolve – that simple forms gradually alter and give rise to more complicated forms – one will naturally wonder how this comes about.

This very question puzzled Charles Darwin, the great naturalist, for many years. He firmly believed in evolution but for a long time was unable to explain it. After many years he produced his celebrated *Theory of Natural Selection* – a theory based on the wonderful ways in which animals are adapted to their surroundings.

Long before Darwin's theory appeared, however, another theory of evolution was put forward. This was developed by Lamarck, a French scientist who lived from 1744 to 1829. According to his theory, if a man trained hard for athletics and built up powerful muscles, his sons would also have strong muscles. In other words, *characters acquired during a lifetime could be inherited.* It is certainly true that constant use of muscles strengthens them and that an unused muscle deteriorates but there is no evidence whatsoever that these features are inherited.

This theory gives no indication of how new structures arise. It implies that an animal develops a structure

Darwin's finches are a group of birds found in the Galapagos Islands. They contributed largely to his theory. There are few other birds and the finches have evolved in several directions, there now being seed-eaters, fruit-eaters, insect eaters, etc. The beaks vary accordingly. Several distinct species and sub-species are recognised. General similarity of structure suggests that they diverged fairly recently from a common ancestor.

THE WOODPECKER FINCH USING A CACTUS SPINE TO EXTRACT INSECTS

VEGETARIAN TREE FINCH

because it needs it. The classic example is that giraffes grew longer necks in order to reach the higher branches. This is, of course, quite wrong. Lamarck's ideas were later disproved by Weissman who showed that acquired characters cannot be inherited. The body cells are quite separate from the reproductive cells and only the latter pass on to the next generation.

Darwin's theory appeared in print in 1859 as the famous 'Origin of Species' although he had previously lectured on his findings and those of Wallace who arrived independently at a similar theory at about the same time. Darwin witnessed the 'struggle for existence' among animals. Most of them produce many offspring but only a few survive. The others succumb to predators and disease: in other words there is 'survival of the fittest'. Darwin also noticed that individuals of a species all vary slightly. All human beings belong to the same species but almost every one can be distinguished by the shape of the ears and nose alone! Such variations make some animals more suited to their surroundings than others. Those best suited are more likely to survive and to reproduce and therefore the favourable variations

46

will be passed on to the next generation. In this way an animal species gradually changes and becomes ideally suited to its surroundings. The latter are always changing however and so natural selection works continuously to produce new forms and, eventually, new species.

Although this theory of Darwin's showed clearly how natural variation was the basis of evolutionary change, there was no explanation of how the variations occurred or how they were inherited. Later work on genetics, however, has shown how the natural variation can come about and also how sudden changes may lead to the appearance of new characteristics.

Genetics and Evolution

Every cell in the body has a certain number of minute thread-like structures called *chromosomes*. For each species there is a fixed number and special processes ensure that each new cell receives its full complement. Each chromosome contains many genes. These are very large molecules that control the features of the whole body. For instance there are genes that control hair-colour, genes that control tooth form, and so on. Sometimes a single gene will be responsible for a feature, sometimes several genes acting together.

During reproduction slightly different combinations of genes are produced. These give rise to the slight (*continuous*) variations among the offspring. Sometimes, however, a gene changes radically – sometimes even a whole chromosome changes, breaks, or disappears. Such sudden changes are called *mutation* and they are responsible for the appearance of new characteristics (i.e. *discontinuous variation*). The

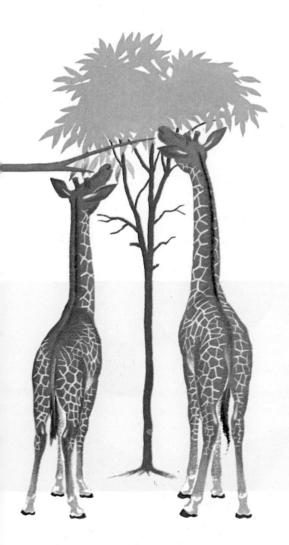

Darwin's theory of Natural Selection can explain the evolution of the giraffe's neck quite easily. The early giraffes competed with other animals for food. The giraffes with the longest necks were able to get better food and thus survived better and produced more offspring. These offspring, too, had longer necks but, more important, they varied among themselves. Selection again acted in favour of those with the longest necks. Over many generations the average neck length increased until the present-day giraffes appeared.

vast majority of mutations are harmful – even lethal – because they interfere with the normal running of the body. Occasionally, however, a useful mutation occurs and is favoured by natural selection. It then becomes incorporated in the normal pattern.

The possibility of mutation was important to the followers of Darwin. It provided the explanations that were lacking in the original theory i.e. the ways in which new structures could be produced for natural selection to act on. Natural selection now provides the complete answer to the question of how evolution has proceeded.

EVOLUTION AT WORK

Several moth species are known to produce occasional black individuals. The gene or genes controlling colour occasionally change so that the black (*melanic*) form appears. Under normal conditions the black form was easily seen by enemies and was eaten but in the last hundred years or so melanic forms have increased in industrial areas. Smoke pollution has blackened buildings and so the occasional mutation was valuable: the black moth was protected by camouflage and gradually increased its numbers as the black gene was passed on to the offspring. The normal form then declined in these areas. This is a good example of Darwin's idea of changing environment leading to the increase of new forms. The new form was not, however, caused by the changing environment.

1850

1950

NORMAL PEPPERED MOTH

MELANIC PEPPERED MOTH

CHAPTER SIX

Convergent and Parallel Evolution

OF whales, Hermann Melville, in his great sea story 'Moby Dick', wrote, 'To be short, then, a whale is *a spouting fish with a horizontal tail*'.

Melville, a seaman and the acutest of observers, was not a trained biologist. Whales do of course resemble fish. They are streamlined in shape. They have a fluked tail, a pair of flippers as fore limbs, and they may even have a dorsal fin along their backs. But in fact whales are mammals; they have warm blood and the females suckle their young with milk. Thus, despite all appearances, they are far more closely related to dogs, rabbits and Man himself than any fish.

One hundred and fifty million years ago another fish-like creature swam the seas. Though it became extinct 70 million years ago, fossils of its bones enable its appearance to be reconstructed. But, far from being a fish, the preserved skeletons show beyond all doubt that the creature was a reptile. Because of its remarkable resemblance to a fish it was called an *ichthyosaur* or fish-lizard (Greek, *ichthys*, a fish; *sauros*, a lizard).

Mammals, reptiles, fishes – three distinct vertebrate groups – but all with members resembling one another. The connecting link between whale, fish and ichthyosaur is that all have lived in the sea.

All have become adapted to an aqueous mode of life. Evolving in the seas, similar types of structure have developed. This evolutionary develop-

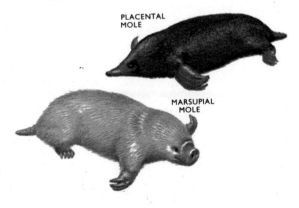

A placental and marsupial mole. Long snouts and powerful claws give these two burrowing animals a remarkably similar appearance.

PLACENTAL MOLE

MARSUPIAL MOLE

Convergent animals may look alike but it is easy to show that they are entirely different creatures with very unlike ancestors – their resemblance in appearance is not due to close relationship. The structures which give the resemblance, often do not develop from a common feature in an ancestor. Thus, the wings of the humming moth are utterly unlike the wings of the humming bird in their origins. Such structures with unrelated origins but with the same functions are said to be *analogous*.

In parallel evolution the very same features possessed by the common ancestor may evolve in very similar ways in the descendants. The two structures, because of this correspondence, are said to be *homologous*. Homologous organs always indicate some common ancestry.

Birds and insects – two groups very far removed from any possible common ancestor. But the similarity of their modes of life has given the humming birds and humming bird hawk moths a close superficial resemblance.

ment, which often leads to apparent likenesses between stocks that have diverged a long way from an original ancestor, is called *convergent evolution* or simply *convergence*.

Convergence is a common phenomenon found in organisms living on land, in water and in the air. It is a powerful witness to the theory of evolution by natural selection. Under the same selective pressures different groups will respond with apparently similar adaptations. Care, then, has to be often taken in classifying animals and plants. Superficial resemblances between two organisms do not necessarily mean that they are closely related.

More Examples of Convergence

Cut off in the continent of Australia, the *marsupials* or pouched mammals have been able to flourish for 150 million years. In most other parts of the world they have disappeared, for competition from the *placental (non-pouched)* mammals proved too much.

Australia offers a wealth of environments, and many different marsupials evolved, filling the niches. The similarity in appearance between the various marsupials and placental mammals provide striking examples of convergence.

Thus Australia has its wolf – the Tasmanian 'wolf'; it has its native 'cat' (*Dasyurus*) and its native 'mouse' feeding procedures.

Another remarkable example is the resemblance between the bill of the duck – a bird – and the bill of the platypus – a mammal. Both creatures obtain food by sifting mud; to perform this function they both have a broad flattened duckbill, giving their heads a similarity in appearance.

Of burrowing creatures, probably the best known is the common earthworm – a long slender creature with no notable structures projecting from its surface. Animals from other groups that have taken up a burrowing mode of life often possess an identical shape. For instance, there are the slow-worms and skinks (really lizards) and the caecilians (really amphibians). The shape and general appearance of the

BEE HUMMING-BIRD

(*Dasycercus*). There are 'ant-eaters' and there are 'sloths'. The flying phalanger is comparable with the flying squirrels and the wombat with ground hogs. Australia even has its own marsupial mole.

Marsupials and placentals are all mammals and do possess a common ancestry in the not-too-remote past. Convergence can, however, produce similarity between completely unrelated creatures. Thus insects and birds are far removed from one another, yet at a glance it is very difficult to tell the difference between a humming bird and a humming moth. Both are the same in size, and both live off nectar in flowers and have converged in their hovering flight and their

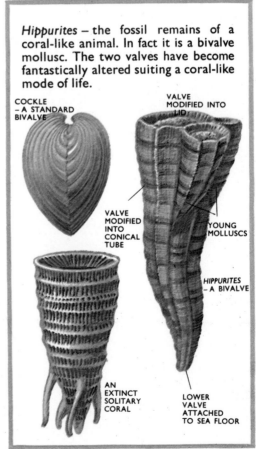

Hippurites – the fossil remains of a coral-like animal. In fact it is a bivalve mollusc. The two valves have become fantastically altered suiting a coral-like mode of life.

COCKLE – A STANDARD BIVALVE

VALVE MODIFIED INTO LID

VALVE MODIFIED INTO CONICAL TUBE

YOUNG MOLLUSCS

HIPPURITES – A BIVALVE

AN EXTINCT SOLITARY CORAL

LOWER VALVE ATTACHED TO SEA FLOOR

Ichthyosaur (reptile) and whale (mammal) and fish — three types of swimming vertebrate. The fore-limbs are all really homologous, showing that the three groups have an ancestry, however remote, in common. The groups have since become widely separated and similarity in appearances, is only a consequence of convergent evolution.

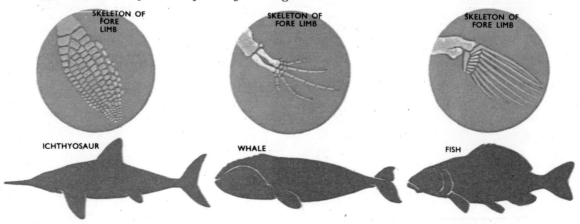

snakes also suggests that they evolved from a burrowing group.

Convergence is not confined to the animal kingdom. Plants exposed to similar outside influences may also resemble one another in the structures they evolve. Hundreds of species of tree make up the three great rain forests of the world. Yet even to a specialist it is often difficult to tell one form from a completely unrelated form. All grow to great heights, lack branches on their lower trunks, develop similarly shaped foliage and similar bark.

In American deserts cacti are characteristic plants. Their stems are swollen with water-storing tissues; they are covered in protective spines and do not carry leaves. Very similar in all these respects are the euphorbias, native to Africa. But despite the cactus-like appearance, euphorbias are not closely related to cacti.

Parallel Evolution

The term *parallel* evolution or *parallelism* also describes a process of similar adaptations under the control of natural selection. In *convergence*, however, ancestries are very different, as close inspection soon reveals. Marsupials are easily distinguished from placentals not only by their pouches but numerous differences in their skeletons.

In parallelism ancestries are not so different. Species evolving from the same ancestor may, instead of steadily increasing their differences, evolve independently along the same lines. The jerboas of African and Asian deserts are rodents especially adapted to their environment. Particularly conspicuous are their long hind legs with which they leap rapidly over the sand. In America another rodent – the kangaroo rat – has almost exactly the same appearance, though it must have evolved entirely separately from the jerboa. Another example of parallel evolution may be seen in the porcupines of South America and those of Africa. In all probability, porcupines evolved from a spineless common ancestor and have developed their spines independently, in the two continents.

CHAPTER SEVEN

Paedomorphosis

A strange transformation astonished biologists in the year 1865. Certain types of 'giant newts' called Axolotls had been brought to the Zoological Gardens in Paris. Blunt nosed, dark in colour, equipped with three pairs of feathery external gills, these amphibians were known to spend the whole of their lives in freshwater. Unlike most amphibians they never came onto land.

But the Paris specimens began to change. The external gills disappeared; so did the crest on the tail. Eyelids appeared and the colour of the skin altered. In place of an Axolotl, there appeared the familiar striped Tiger Salamander, a common amphibian throughout the eastern regions of the United States.

Immediately it became clear that Axolotls were really a race of 'permanent larvae'. They lived to become sexually mature yet they never lost certain of their larval characteristics. The reason for this incomplete development was at first a mystery. Today the reason is thought to be due to lack of iodine in some lake waters.

Other examples of Salamander larvae that do not usually complete their development became recognized. Some such as *Necturus* the mud-puppy of the Eastern United States, are permanently larval in form. No matter what conditions surround them, they keep their larval appearance.

The life of an individual animal usually commences as a single fertilized cell. By division the cell produces numerous other cells. These are arranged to form the tissues and organs of the new creature. The complete life history of the individual, from egg, through embryonic stages, and immature juvenile stages to the mature adult is called its *ontogeny*.

Changes caused by recombination or alteration of genes can occur at any stage in the life history. Another factor that can change is the time and the

Left, the adult tunicate or sea squirt is rather sponge-like in appearance; but its larva – resembling a tadpole – has gill slits, a dorsal nerve chord and a notochord. By failing to develop into the adult, could not such a larva give rise to higher chordate animals such as the first fishes?

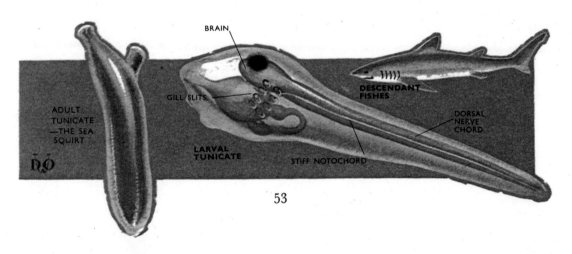

BRAIN

GILL SLITS

DESCENDANT FISHES

ADULT TUNICATE —THE SEA SQUIRT

LARVAL TUNICATE

STIFF NOTOCHORD

DORSAL NERVE CHORD

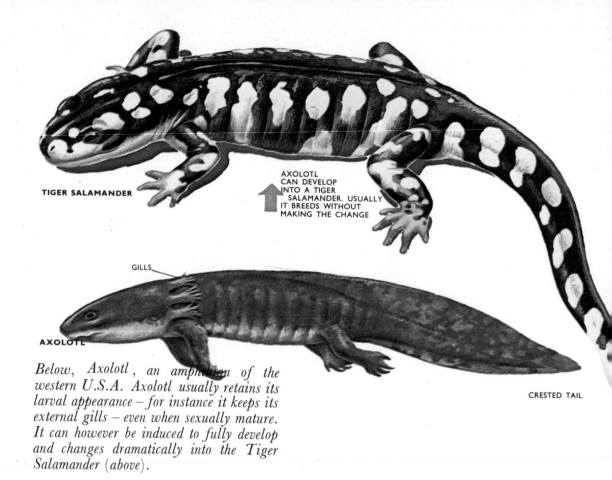

TIGER SALAMANDER

AXOLOTL
CAN DEVELOP
INTO A TIGER
SALAMANDER. USUALLY
IT BREEDS WITHOUT
MAKING THE CHANGE

GILLS

AXOLOTL

CRESTED TAIL

Below, Axolotl, an amphibian of the western U.S.A. Axolotl usually retains its larval appearance – for instance it keeps its external gills – even when sexually mature. It can however be induced to fully develop and changes dramatically into the Tiger Salamander (above).

order in which various structures develop (*heterochrony*). Through the slowing down or speeding up of the processes of development, marked effects can be made on the final stages of the life history of an animal. Thus in the instance of the axolotl, certain larval characters are retained in the otherwise sexually mature animal. This retention is called *Neoteny*. An extreme case of neoteny – when the sexually mature animal is larval in every other respect is called Paedogenesis. The two processes Neoteny and Paedogenesis are commonly referred to as *Paedomorphosis*.

The process of paedomorphosis has come to throw great light on evolution. In effect, new forms of animal can be produced from old forms. The appear-

ance of a sexually mature descendant could differ markedly from the appearance of the sexually mature ancestor. Rather would the descendant resemble in appearance the young stage of its ancestor.

From an evolutionary viewpoint there are great potential advantages. The larval structures, once they have become persistent, have an increased time in which they can further develop; new variations of the structure may appear. Because former adult characters no longer appear, genes of these lost characters are possibly available for new variations.

By paedomorphosis and the sudden appearance of evolutionary novelties, completely new lineages could have branched off from older lines.

Possible Origin for the Vertebrates

Tunicates, or sea squirts, are small, barrel-shaped creatures which usually live anchored to the sea floor. The only prominent structural features to be seen from the outside are an opening at the top through which water is wafted and an opening at one side through which the water flows out. From the water passing through minute food particles are filtered. Certainly there seems little similarity between the adult tunicate and the backboned animals such as the fish and amphibians. But some tunicates possess a mobile larva. It is rather like a tadpole with a large head and an oscillating tail. The activity of the larva means that there is the possibility that new areas can be colonized by the tunicates.

The internal structure of the tunicate larva is very interesting. Along the upper (*dorsal*) surface there is a hard but flexible bar called a notochord. Above it lies a hollow nerve cord, while in the head is a rudimentary brain. These are characters of all higher vertebrate creatures. Is the relationship more than coincidental? When the 'tadpole' finally settles down and develops into the adult tunicate these characters are lost. Should the fixed way of life be lost altogether by paedomorphosis the way would then be open for the 'larva' to give rise to the first fishlike vertebrates.

Gaps in the Fossil Record

Darwin's theory of evolution explains how the more complicated organs could arise from simpler ones. A continuous series of organisms should theoretically have existed linking descendant stocks with their ancestors. The fossil record – the preserved remains of animals which have lived in the past – is the most obvious place to look for 'missing links'. A few finds have been successful but generally creatures which link together whole divisions of the animal kingdom are rare.

If paedomorphosis has played a part in evolution, as is likely, such 'missing links' could be accounted for. Paedomorphosis *demands* fossil gaps. By retarding developmental processes, quite abrupt modifications could take place. The millions of years

---

Theory of Recapitulation

In 1866 Haeckel put forward his theory of Recapitulation or Biogentic Law. 'The life history of an individual' argued Haeckel 'recapitulates the whole of its ancestry.' For example, the embryo of Man passes from a single-celled state through stages resembling fishes, amphibians and reptiles. Haeckel's theory has been proved completely untrue. The embryo of Man never resembles the adult of any other creature that ever lived. But the embryo does bear a semblance to the embryos of other vertebrates; this denotes a related ancestry.

There are occasionally instances which would seem to support Haeckel's theory. Sometimes adult structures can be pushed back into the young stages of a descendant. This is due to another process of heterochrony called *Acceleration*. Unlike paedomorphosis, acceleration is of no real evolutionary importance.

Commonly, embryonic features persist into the adult animal with progressive development and change – a process of heterochrony called *Deviation*. When structures which function in the young stages are lost in the adult – for instance the tails of frogs – the process is one of *Reduction*.

Left, feathers of the ostrich resemble the fledgling down feathers of other birds. They are probably neotenous features. So probably are the drooping ears of many domestic dogs, which resemble the ears of young wolf cubs.

FEATHER OR 'PLUME' OF FLIGHTLESS OSTRICH

DOWN FEATHER PREDOMINANT IN FLEDGLINGS

HARRIER ONE OF THE MANY BREEDS OF DOG HAVING DROOPING EARS

YOUNG WOLF CUB – EARS DROOPING

required for evolution would not be necessary as there would be no gradual changes. Gaps between annelid worms and molluscs, are probably account ed for by paedomorphosis.

Fossil evidence does in some instances support paedomorphosis. Young stages of trilobite preserved in ancient rock closely resemble in appearance the adult forms of later trilobites. Similar evidence is found in remains of the fossil graptolites and ammonites.

Paedomorphosis and Man

The embryo of the anthropod apes has the following characters – a relatively high brain weight in comparison with the rest of their body, scanty hair, and a flat face. Further the foramen magnum (the orifice with which the vertebral column articulates with the head) has a forward position underneath the skull. Consequently the head is balanced more upright on the spine than in the adult apes. Is there not something rather familiar about these characters? There is – they are all characters which distinguish Man.

This close similarity between Man and a foetal ape is probably much more than coincidence. It seems extremely likely that in the remote past, the retention of early embryonic stages, with the consequent non-appearance of specialized adult features, led to the branching off of human stock from an anthropoid-like ancestor.

The larvae of myriapods (centipedes, and millipedes) only have a few segments and three pairs of well-developed legs. At this stage they bear a strong resemblance to insects. Insects may well stem from such larval forms by paedomorphosis.

LARVAL MILLIPEDE (A MYRIAPOD)

INSECT (A SPRINGTAIL)

Anthropology

CHAPTER EIGHT

Man in the Past

THE ORIGINS OF MAN

The primates (the animal group to which Man belongs) first appeared about 70 million years ago at the beginning of the Tertiary period.

The early primates were small shrew-like creatures. They evolved along several lines and by Eocene times several groups of primates were in existence. Some of these groups resembled the modern lemurs and tarsiers. In the latter part of the Eocene a group of tarsiers began to change and in the Oligocene they gave rise to monkeys and the earliest apes. The latter were unspecialised animals but they evolved in several directions (*radiated*), and Miocene deposits in Africa contain a wide variety of fossil apes. These all had slender limbs and were obviously not specialised for life in the trees. They were probably very agile on the ground. There was a further radiation in late Miocene times and the apes spread into Europe and Asia. A common genus was *Dryopithecus*, which contained species resembling all the modern apes. These animals were obviously forerunners of the present-day species. The origins of Man almost certainly lie in this group, but the fossil record is not yet good enough to establish definite links.

Africa must have been an important centre of primate evolution during Pliocene times too, for early Pleistocene deposits in Bechuanaland have yielded some remarkable man-ape fossils. In 1925 Prof. Raymond Dart reported the discovery of a skull which, although ape-like in general appearance, had several human characteristics. Other similar fossils have since been found and a fairly complete picture of these animals is available. The brain was of about 600 cubic centimetres – about the size of a modern gorilla brain, which is less than half that of a modern human brain. The jaws were large and ape-like and the forehead was low (i.e. the frontal lobes of the brain were small). Teeth were arranged

Pithecanthropus skull (centre) is intermediate between that of the gorilla (left) and that of Homo sapiens (right).

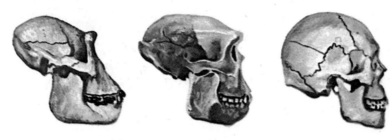

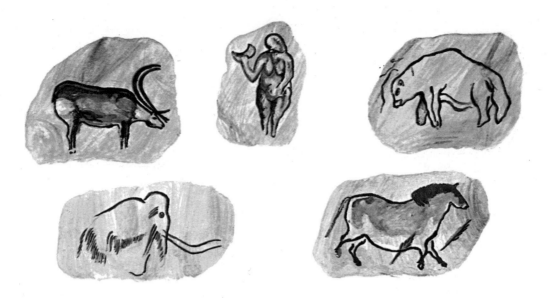

Cave Paintings of Aurignacian Man

very much as in Man but were large; the head was held more erect than in apes. Other remains show that these creatures walked in an upright position and were about the size of modern pygmies. They were almost certainly hunting animals. These South African man-apes form the genus *Australopithecus*.

The boundary between apes and Man is not very distinct. Man has several special features which have helped him to become master of the Earth. These include: erect posture, free movement of the hand and forearm, sharp sight, a reasoning brain and the power of speech. These features are to some extent shared with the apes and have been acquired gradually. The most practical dividing line is the appearance of manufactured tools which are permanent indications of some form of intelligence. Various pebbles associated with *Australopithecus* remains may have been used as tools. Whether we call the Australopithecines men or not, it is clear that by early Pleistocene times

primate evolution had reached the level of a near-human body although the brain still lagged behind.

During the last fifty years a number of fossils have been found in Java and near Peking in China. They date from about mid-Pleistocene times and are placed in the genus *Pithecanthropus*. They are best known as Java and Peking Man. There was some variation in brain size but it was between that of the larger apes and modern man (*Homo sapiens*). The skulls retained a number of ape-like features such as heavy projecting jaws and eyebrow ridges but the teeth and the rest of the skeleton were definitely of human form. *Pithecanthropus* was shorter than modern man and walked upright. He made numerous stone tools and knew how to make fire. He also probably had a fairly simple language and some sort of social life. Like the Australopithecines, he was a hunter. Various skulls have been found in Asia, Africa and Europe showing a range of characters between those of *Pithecan-*

thropus and *Homo*. Men of the *Pithecanthropus* type were obviously widespread in mid-Pleistocene times and probably gradually gave rise to men of the genus *Homo*.

Because of their permanent nature, Man's stone tools are rather better known than Man himself during the Pleistocene. All the stone tools made during this period were produced by chipping flints, but as time progressed the technique improved and a number of distinct stages can be seen in the fossil record. **The whole period of stone chipping is called the** *Old Stone Age* **or** *Palaeolithic*. During the Upper Palaeolithic a wide variety of wooden and bone tools were in common use as well as stone tools.

Europe in *Mousterian* times (see diagram) was inhabited by a very distinctive type of man – *Homo neanderthalensis* or *Neanderthal man*. Many fossils are known and it was once thought that the Neanderthals were direct ancestors of man. They had heavy jaws and brow-ridges, a thick neck and heavy bones and were ape-like in appearance. The ape-like characters increased in the later Neanderthals and it is now clear that they were a side-branch of human evolution. There is evidence for the existence of Neanderthals in Africa and Asia at the same time.

At some time during *Aurignacian* times the European Neanderthals were completely replaced by a modern type called *Cro-Magnon* men after the place in France where they were first discovered. They probably originated in Asia and then, with a superior organisation, spread and wiped out the Neanderthals. Cro-Magnon men left many stone tools and cave paintings in France and Spain. These indicate a hunting life and a social existence. In many ways Cro-Magnon men must have been like the present-day Bushmen of Africa. Their art and their tools are very similar. There is some evidence in the fossil record of various races of Man at this time.

Since the origin of Cro-Magnon man, *Homo sapiens* has not progressed very far physically but there have been great cultural changes through the Neolithic age, when Man learnt how to grind and polish stones, through the Bronze and Iron ages to the present-day Atomic age.

Palaeolithic man was essentially a hunter and gatherer of wild foods. One of the most important advances was the discovery of agriculture which enabled Man to abandon his nomadic existence and settle down. Speech and writing are difficult to date but probably progressed side by side with tool-making and social life. Communication in this way must obviously have gained in importance when Man settled down to agricultural pursuits.

Time scale showing the approximate durations of the ice-ages (blue bands) and the succession of stone tools in Europe. The fossil men are not all from Europe.

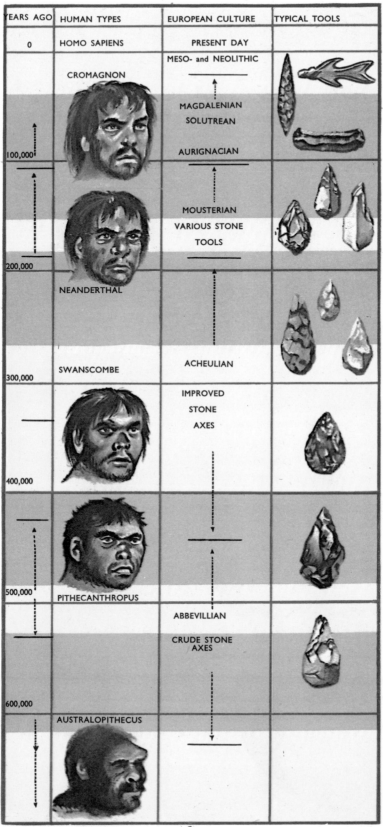

YEARS AGO	HUMAN TYPES	EUROPEAN CULTURE	TYPICAL TOOLS
0	HOMO SAPIENS	PRESENT DAY	
	CROMAGNON	MESO- and NEOLITHIC	
100,000		MAGDALENIAN SOLUTREAN AURIGNACIAN	
200,000		MOUSTERIAN VARIOUS STONE TOOLS	
	NEANDERTHAL		
300,000	SWANSCOMBE	ACHEULIAN	
		IMPROVED STONE AXES	
400,000			
500,000	PITHECANTHROPUS		
		ABBEVILLIAN CRUDE STONE AXES	
600,000			
	AUSTRALOPITHECUS		

When the reign of the dinosaurs came to an end, the mammals took over the Earth and evolved along a number of lines. One of these lines led to the monkeys and apes – the *primates*. During Miocene and Pliocene times (less than 25 million years ago) there were many small apes in Africa and Asia. Numerous fossils have been found, some of which resemble the Orang and gibbons while others are more like the modern chimps. It is reasonable to assume that these various fossil types gave rise eventually to the modern apes. Somewhere here, too, must lie the ancestors of Man, but for a long time nothing was known of the stages by which Man might have emerged from ape-like ancestors.

Then, in 1924, came a remarkable discovery. In a limestone cave in

A comparison of the skulls of a gorilla (A) Australopithecus *(B), and modern Man (C). The small brain case and the protruding jaws of* Australopithecus *are clearly seen.*

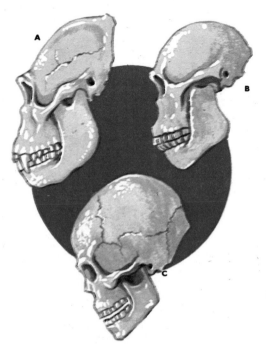

Bechuanaland a skull was discovered during quarrying. It was passed to Prof. Raymond Dart for examination. Although it was incomplete, the skull was sufficient for Professor Dart to realize that it showed a strange combination of ape-like and human characteristics. He called the creature *Australopithecus* which means 'southern ape' and regarded it as a link between apes and men. Since then, several more skulls and other bones have been found. Some have been given various other names such as *Paranthropus* and *Zinjanthropus* but are all of the same general type and are included in the same family as *Australopithecus*. These finds have enabled scientists to make a good reconstruction of the animals.

The skulls of some of the Australopithecines are ape-like in appearance with large brow ridges. The size is about that of a modern chimpanzee. Some of the skulls are of young individuals but the brain probably grew to about 600 c.c. – about the size of a modern gorilla brain, and less than half that of modern Man. In spite of their chimp-like appearance the skulls show many human characteristics. The teeth are arranged in a parabolic arch just as in Man and the eye-tooth or *canine* is small and not protruding like that of apes. In modern apes the skull is held forward and supported by large and powerful neck muscles which are attached to large ridges, on the skull. These ridges are small in the *Australopithecus* skull and this suggests that it was balanced more as in modern Man. Further evidence for this is the position of the *foramen magnum* – the hole through which the spinal cord leaves the skull. The opening is further under the skull than in the apes.

The evidence of the skull, therefore, suggests that *Australopithecus* walked with his head upright as modern Man. Further evidence to support an upright posture comes from the various limb bones and hip bones that have been found. The thigh bones (femurs) resemble those of modern Man and indicate that these ancient creatures walked erect but even more important is the evidence from the hip-bones.

In Man, the ilium or blade of the hip-bone is broad and serves as an attachment for the large buttock muscles. These muscles serve to raise the trunk on the legs, and are thus essential for an upright posture.

Many of the Australopithecine fossils have been found in cave deposits. The presence of baboon skulls together with various sticks and stones indicates that Australopithecus *may have hunted the baboons with these primitive weapons.*

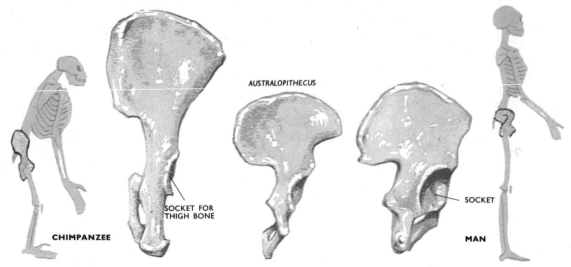

CHIMPANZEE   SOCKET FOR THIGH BONE   AUSTRALOPITHECUS   SOCKET   MAN

The right side of the pelvis of a chimpanzee (left), Australopithecus *and Man (right). The pelvis of* Australopithecus *is almost human and indicates an upright stance for these creatures.*

Modern apes do not normally walk erect and their hip bones have a long narrow blade. The ilium of *Australopithecus* was broad and very similar to that of modern Man. The size of the bones suggests that *Australopithecus* was about the size of a present-day pygmy. Bones of the arm are essentially human in form and lack the ridges found on

AUSTRALOPITHECUS   MAN

EARLY AUSTRALO-PITHECINES

MODERN APES

10 MILLION YEARS AGO?

EARLY APES

A SIMPLIFIED TREE SHOWING THE POSSIBLE RELATIONSHIPS OF THE KNOWN AUSTRALOPITHECINES

the arm bones of apes. From this it is assumed that *Australopithecus* walked on the ground and did not swing in the trees. The ridges on the arm bones of apes support the muscles necessary for swinging.

From the available fossils, anthropologists have built up a fairly good picture of these 'southern apes'. They were about five feet tall and walked about in an upright position with the head held well back on the neck. The face and skull, however, were ape-like, indicating that the human posture developed before the human brain. Were these ancient creatures advanced apes or primitive men? It is difficult to answer this question but, on balance, they seem to deserve the name primitive Man, rather than ape. One criterion for separating Man from other animals, is tool-making. There is no definite evidence of this associated with *Australopithecus* but numerous baboon skulls have been found nearby with battered parts. This suggests the use of stones or other weapons to kill prey – an elementary tool usage. There is no evidence that they used fire, however.

The apes are generally forest and tree-dwellers, while Man, including *Australopithecus*, lives on the ground, walking on his two feet. How did this change come about? Why should tree-swinging apes have started to walk on the ground? The known fossils are now believed to be more than one million years old (Lower Pleistocene Age). The group as a whole must have been in existence long before that. Professor von Koenigswald has suggested that perhaps ten million years ago a group of apes broke away from the main line. At first, there was probably not much difference between the two lines but one line became able to walk about on the ground.

As the climate cooled down (a trend culminating in the Great Ice Age) the dense forests were pushed back towards the Equator. With them went the typical apes but the ones that were

The arrangement of the teeth of, left to right, a gorilla, Australopithecus, *and Man. The arrangement in* Australopithecus *is almost identical to that in Man.*

less dependent on the trees were able to live in the more open country that was left. They were able to walk about and probably began to capture animal food using their free hands. These creatures were the early Australopithecines.

Modern types of Man are known to have been in existence 500 thousand years ago. It is believed that these evolved as an offshoot from the early Australopithecines and that the Australopithecine fossils are not direct ancestors of modern men.

PITHECANTHROPUS

In 1891, while excavating at Trinil in Java, a Dutch doctor and anthropologist named Eugene Dubois discovered part of a skull and a tooth. This was the start of the study of fossil Man. One of the most remarkable things about the discovery was that Dubois had predicted that fossil men would be found in that region of the world. The skull fragment had large brow ridges and Dubois believed that it belonged to an ape. However, the following year, in almost exactly the same place, he discovered a thigh bone. This bone was essentially modern in form and its owner obviously walked erect as present-day

Man does. Dubois was convinced that the skull and the thigh bone came from the same individual and he named his new find *Pithecanthropus erectus*, meaning 'upright ape-man', for he believed it was a sort of halfway stage between apes and modern Man. From these scanty remains he described the creature as '. . . a Man-like species of Transitional Anthropoid . . .'

Dubois met with much opposition when he announced his discovery. Some anthropologists refused to believe that the skull and the thigh bone came from the same type of animal. They could not accept that an animal with an ape-like skull could have such

modern limb bones. The discovery of the African Australopithecine or 'Southern Ape' fossils in 1924, however, showed that long before *Pithecanthropus* or 'Java Man' came on the scene, creatures were walking erect although their brains were no larger than those of apes. Further finds in Java have now confirmed that a primitive man existed in that region about half a million years ago. They also show that Dubois' description of *Pithecanthropus* was basically correct.

Java Man

The later finds of *Pithecanthropus* material – mainly discovered by Pro-

A reconstruction of Java Man in his natural surroundings.

fessor von Koenigswald and his associates – are not all from the same rock layers and represent more than one species. They are, however, sufficiently similar to be placed in the single genus *Pithecanthropus*. From these remains a fairly clear picture has been built up of what these early men looked like.

Java Man was fairly short – about five feet in height – and walked upright as we do today. This information is gained from the size and structure of the limb bones. He had large eye-brow ridges and no real forehead – the top of the skull sloped back from the eyebrows. Reconstructions of the

brain-case indicate that the average volume of the adult brain was probably about 900 cc. This is considerably larger than the brain of an ape but much smaller than that of modern Man (averaging 1350 cc.). The size of the brain suggests that Java Man was not very intelligent although he appears to have made crude stone tools. There is no evidence that Java Man used fire.

He was a hunter and lived largely on various antelopes and other animals whose bones are common in the same rock deposits. He probably moved about in small bands in search of food. The presence of tiny ridges inside the lower jaw is believed by some people to indicate that the tongue was anchored as in modern Man and could therefore move freely. This, together with the form of the brain, suggests that Java Man had at least a primitive sort of language. The evidence, however, is not sufficient to be certain about this.

At about the time of Java Man there must have been a giant man in that area. It is known only from a jaw fragment and a few very large teeth. Apart from their size, these remains resemble those of *Pithecanthropus*. This giant has been called *Meganthropus* (= great man) but no further remains have been found and his size is unknown.

Pekin Man

While supervising excavations near Pekin in 1927, Professor Davidson Black discovered a single human tooth. He realised that it belonged to a type of fossil Man which he called *Sinanthropus* (= China Man). Before long, other remains came to light – mainly skulls and teeth, but with a few limb bones. These show that Pekin Man

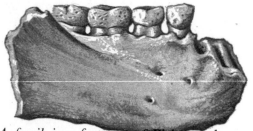

A fossil jaw fragment of Pithecanthropus. From this sort of remains, the whole skull has been reconstructed.

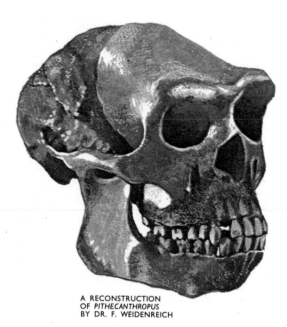

A RECONSTRUCTION
OF *PITHECANTHROPUS*
BY DR. F. WEIDENREICH

Pithecanthropus *skull (above) compared with modern Man. The heavy brow ridges, lack of forehead and projecting jaws are important features.*

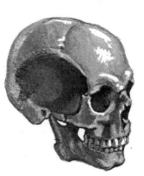

(*Sinanthropus*) walked erect and was very similar to Java Man. There is much variation in brain size but the average volume is just over a thousand cubic centimetres – a little larger than that of Java Man. Pekin Man made stone tools and used fire. Chipped stones together with ash and charred bones have been found in their caves.

Pekin Man lived somewhat later than Java Man – about three hundred thousand years ago – but the general similarity of the two has led to their both being included in the genus *Pithecanthropus*. Pekin Man is now known officially as *Pithecanthropus pekinensis*.

The Relationships of *Pithecanthropus*

Although *Pithecanthropus* shows a number of connections with the apes there is no doubt that he was a true Man. Apart from a recent report of a tool-making Man living in Tanganyika nearly two million years ago, Java Man is the earliest undisputed fossil Man. What is known of his descent and his later evolution?

The 'Southern Ape' or Australopithecine fossils of Africa, including *Australopithecus* and *Zinjanthropus*, are believed to be about a million years old. Their brains were little larger than those of apes but their limbs and posture were very similar to modern Man. The skull was ape-like but it showed a number of human features and although it is difficult to be sure, these creatures seem to merit the name of primitive men.

Could these ancient creatures have been the ancestors of *Pithecanthropus?* This is unlikely. In his very heavy brow-ridges and some other features,

Pithecanthropus is more ape-like. Even more important is the time factor. The Australopithecines lived about half a million years before Java Man. It is highly unlikely that the differences could have arisen in such a comparatively short time. It is possible that the Australopithecines are very close to the line of human ancestry but still on a side-branch. Both they and *Pithecanthropus* probably had a common ape-like ancestor even further back in time.

At Ternifine in Algeria some jaw bones have been found showing some resemblances to the jaws of *Pithecanthropus*. It is probable that men of this general type were widespread between three hundred thousand and five hundred thousand years ago. A large jaw-bone unearthed in Germany has been ascribed to 'Heidelberg Man'. It shows some similarities to the Algerian fossils but is more modern in appearance. Skull fragments found at Swanscombe in England and at Steinheim in Germany are about the same age (three hundred thousand years). Both closely resemble modern Man (*Homo sapiens*) but the Steinheim skull has powerful brow-ridges like *Pithecanthropus*. It would appear that the *Pithecanthropus* type gradually evolved into modern Man in the Old World. The available evidence, however, is not enough to prove these theories and we must await further fossil discoveries.

The possible relationships of Pithecanthropus, *as ancestors of modern Man.* (Right) *Some stone tools found with remains of Java Man.*

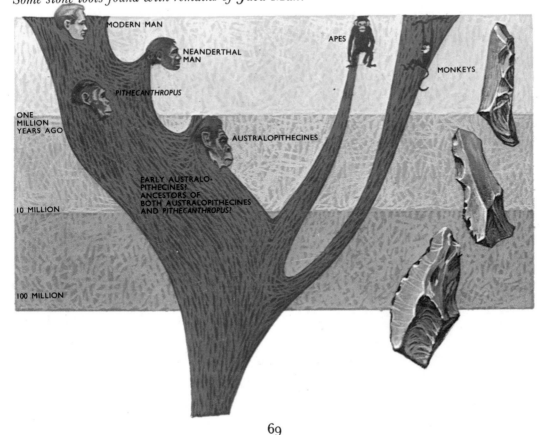

Neanderthal man typifies the popular conception of primitive man – rugged and somewhat ape-like, yet sufficiently human to fully justify the term 'man'. He takes his name from the Neander Valley near Dusseldorf in Germany, where the first properly-studied remains were found in 1856.

These remains – consisting of a piece of skull and a few other bones – were the first to be recognized as fossil man, but other, earlier-found, fossils that were not studied at the time have now been shown to be remains of Neanderthal man. The Dusseldorf remains showed similarities with both man and apes and anthropologists regarded Neanderthal man as a stage in the evolution of modern man from apes. Thomas Huxley, in his book 'Man's Place in Nature', compared the apes and Man and showed how the then recently-discovered fossils fitted into the proposed pattern of evolution. If the Dusseldorf fossils alone had come to light, we might still have regarded *Homo neanderthalensis* as our direct ancestor. But many more fossils have been found, thanks largely to the Neanderthals' habit of burying their dead, and the theory has had to be altered to fit the facts.

Remains of more than 50 individual Neanderthals have been found, some of them almost complete skeletons – like the 'old man of La Chapelle', a nearly perfect skeleton of an old man found in a cave in the Dordogne region of France. All of the Neanderthal fossils date from the third interglacial period or the early part of the last ice advance, giving them an antiquity of between 100 and 200 thousand years.

The fact that most of the skeletons have been found in caves has led to the

Skull of Neanderthal Man compared with skull of modern Man. The foramen magnum was farther back than in modern Man so that the skull would have been carried in a more forward position. The brow ridges were far more massive and the skull bones generally thicker.

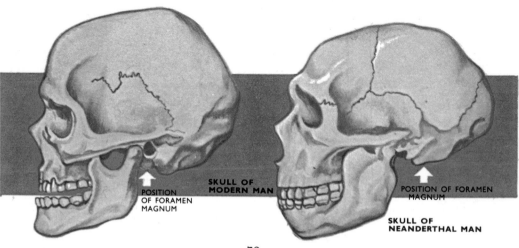

inevitable belief that Neanderthal Man was a cave dweller. This is not necessarily so, however, for it may be that they just preferred to bury their dead in caves, or that remains are preserved better in caves. Archaeologists, too, concentrate on cave deposits and so it follows that most of their finds come from caves. Neanderthal Man certainly entered caves and probably lived in them at times, but there is no proof that he *always* lived in them.

Examination of the skeletal remains and associated tools or artefacts has enabled scientists to build up a fairly complete picture of what Neanderthal man was like and what sort of life he led.

The typical Neanderthal barely topped five feet in height but the limb bones were thick and heavy, indicating a powerful and muscular body rather like that of the modern apes. He is frequently pictured in a stooping attitude but the evidence for this is not conclusive and the stoop has probably been exaggerated. The bones of the lower leg suggest that he often squatted on his haunches as many children do today.

The skull must have been carried in a more forward position than that of modern Man, for the *foramen magnum* (through which the spinal cord passes) was farther back than in modern Man. Confirmation of this posture is provided by the neck vertebrae which have very long 'spines', presumably to anchor the large muscles necessary to balance the head in its forward position. The skull as a whole was large, with an average brain size of about 1,450 cubic centimetres (millilitres) – compared with 1,350 cc for the average modern human brain. The shape of the skull, however, showed certain

Complete skeletons of modern Man and Neanderthal Man compared. Neanderthal Man, carrying his head in a more forward position, did not walk fully upright. His stoop, however, has often been exaggerated. Neanderthal skeletons are common in Europe but similar forms have also been found in South Africa and Java.

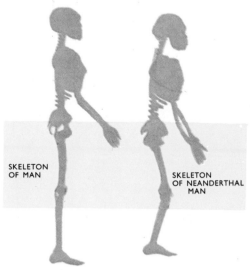

SKELETON OF MAN

SKELETON OF NEANDERTHAL MAN

primitive features. The skull bones were thick and there were relatively **huge brow ridges above the eye sockets. There was not much of a** fore-head, the brain case sloping gradually back from the eyes. The jaws protruded and the lower one sloped backwards from the mouth without forming a chin. The shape and arrangement of the teeth was essentially human but they were of a larger size than that generally found in modern Man.

During the life of an individual, the bone surfaces and joints undergo changes and the amount of change, such as the closing up of the skull joints, is a good guide to the age of the individual. The state of the bones of the Neanderthal fossils indicates that few of them lived to a good age – even the so-called 'old man of La Chapelle' died at about forty. Lack of hygiene must have resulted in a lot of disease which, together with the danger from wild animals and, especially in the colder periods, starvation, probably resulted in early death. Female skeletons are more rarely found and few Stone Age women seem to have even reached the age of thirty.

Tool-making among the Neanderthals

The Neanderthals used quite a wide range of stone tools, fashioned mainly from flint. The tools were sufficiently different from those of earlier periods for a separate culture period to be established. Typical collections of tools were found in a cave at Le Moustier in the Dordogne, and the name 'Mousterian' has been given to this period of stone age culture. Neanderthal Man has, accordingly, also been called Mousterian Man.

Most of the tools were made from flakes of flint by carefully chipping the edges. This produced scraping and cutting tools for use in skinning and cutting up the animals that had been killed for food and skins. Some of the early Mousterian hand-axes bear signs of having been derived from the earlier Acheulian traditions.

Neanderthal Man used fire regularly and it probably served several purposes – to keep him warm, to drive away wolves and other carnivores, and to sharpen the points of the hunters' wooden spears. Broken bones seem to have been used for tools and weapons but there is no evidence that the

Neanderthals had mastered the art of shaping bone.

Hunting and Social Life

Other bones associated with the Neanderthal remains indicate the sort of food on which the Neanderthals existed. Many of the animals that they hunted were very large and it is obvious that *Homo neanderthalensis* must have worked in groups to capture

72

Some activities of Neanderthal Man. Top left, cleaning an animal skin with a stone scraper. Right, hunting wild animals provided Neanderthal Man with food. Bottom, fashioning stone tools and hardening the points of wooden spears by fire.

these animals. Wild boar, ibex, cave bear, rhinoceros, and even elephant figured in the diet of the Neanderthals, according to the animal bones found with the human remains. Naturally, not all these animals were hunted at one period. Changing climates brought various animals within reach of the Neanderthals.

The animals were probably killed largely with the wooden spears that had been sharpened in the fire, but the occurrence of some large battered skulls suggests another possible method of hunting. These skulls, notably those of the cave bear, have been found in association with some large boulders and it is likely that the Neanderthals stood high above the bears' runs and rolled the boulders down onto the animals. Larger creatures, such as the rhino and elephant, were possibly killed in pit traps.

Neanderthal Man probably worked

in family groups of twenty or more individuals and it is highly unlikely that they could have done this without at least some sort of language. Although the brain was of a simple form compared with that of modern Man, the regions corresponding to that concerning speech in *Homo sapiens* were probably well developed. It can be assumed that Neanderthal Man could speak though whether he reached a very high level of articulation is not certain.

Distribution of Neanderthals

The remains of typical Neanderthals are found over large areas of Europe and neighbouring parts of Asia and North Africa but the Neanderthaloid type was by no means confined to these areas. Rhodesian Man, whose skull and other bones were found at Broken Hill in Northern Rhodesia in 1921, is clearly related to Neanderthal Man, although there are some differences in the structure of the limb bones. The geological evidence indicates that Rhodesian Man lived at a later date than the typical Neanderthals. The associated stone tools are of a more primitive type than the Mousterian implements of Europe, but this is of no great significance, for cultures of this sort take some time to spread and a primitive tool may still be in use in one area centuries after it had been superseded in others.

Skulls of Solo Man – found in late Ice Age deposits on the banks of the Solo River in Java – also show numerous resemblances to the Neanderthals, but they are not complete enough to make detailed comparisons. It is likely that both Rhodesian and Solo Men were merely variants of the Neanderthal stock, and like it, became extinct.

The Relationships of Neanderthal Man

The previous paragraph showed that men of the Neanderthal types were widespread during the third interglacial and the early part of the last ice advance. Fossils from an even earlier period show a number of similarities with both Neanderthals and the older *Pithecanthropus* of the mid-Pleistocene. It seems that *Pithecanthropus* gave rise to the generalized Neanderthal type during the latter part of the Pleistocene. When the first Neanderthal fossils were studied it was assumed that the creature was a stage in the evolution of Modern Man, and, if further discoveries had not been made, it is likely that we would still hold this view, for the Dusseldorf fossils certainly show a mixture of ape-like and human characters. We now believe, however, that the Neanderthals were no more than cousins of modern Man and there is plenty of evidence to support this.

The earliest Neanderthal fossils known are only about 200,000 years old, yet, before this, there were creatures, such as Swanscombe Man, that showed modern characteristics. The brain of the typical Neanderthal was larger than that of modern Man and it is highly unlikely that it would have become smaller again during evolution. Another very important point is that the later Neanderthals became progressively more heavily built – the jaws and brow-ridges developed and the creatures become more and more unlike *Homo sapiens*. This is quite the reverse of what would be expected if the Neanderthals were the ancestors of modern Man. Finally, the Neanderthals were replaced in

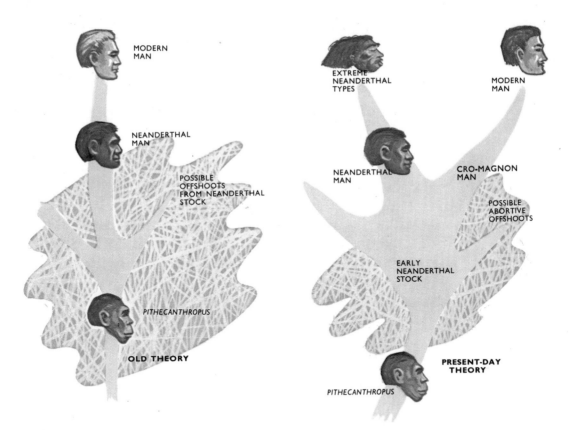

MODERN
MAN

NEANDERTHAL
MAN

POSSIBLE
OFFSHOOTS
FROM NEANDERTHAL
STOCK

PITHECANTHROPUS

OLD THEORY

EXTREME
NEANDERTHAL
TYPES

MODERN
MAN

NEANDERTHAL
MAN

CRO-MAGNON
MAN

POSSIBLE
ABORTIVE
OFFSHOOTS

EARLY
NEANDERTHAL
STOCK

**PRESENT-DAY
THEORY**

PITHECANTHROPUS

Left, old idea of Neanderthal Man's relationship with modern Man. Neanderthal Man was considered an intermediate stage in the evolution from Pithecanthropus to modern Man. Right, today's generally-held theory – Neanderthal Man probably evolved in a line parallel to that of modern Man. Both lines spring from a common stock so that Neanderthal Man becomes Man's cousin – not his direct ancestor.

Europe, very suddenly by a modern type of Man—Cro-Magnon man, who almost all schools of thought now accept as the immediate predecessor of modern man. There was no gradual change such as would have occurred if one had evolved into the other. The Mousterian tools were succeeded suddenly in the deposits by Aurignacian tools of Cro-Magnon man who must have reached Europe from elsewhere and killed or driven out the Neanderthals. Neanderthals in other parts of the world were probably replaced soon afterwards and, as far as his physical characters were concerned, Man's evolution was complete.

It is believed that the *Pithecanthropus* type gave rise to the Neanderthal type but that, before the typical Neanderthal characteristics had evolved, the line split into two. One branch led to the extreme Neanderthals and the other to *Homo sapiens* so that the typical Neanderthal cannot be regarded as a direct ancestor of Modern Man. He belonged to a side-line of evolution which died out without leaving any descendants.

CHAPTER NINE

Present-day Man

THE LIVING STONE AGE

What was life like for our Stone Age ancestors? Some of the most interesting information can be gained from various present-day tribes. There are a number of these in isolated parts of the world using tools similar to those which were in use at various times in prehistoric Europe. We can assume therefore that – allowing for some interference by civilized man – their way of life resembles that of our ancestors.

The simplest present-day cultures are represented by the Australian Aborigines, the South African Bushmen and various Asian and American tribes. Their culture is of Palaeolithic type and all of them live by hunting animals and gathering wild fruits and vegetables. Their very lives depend upon their skill at hunting and their ability to find food, for there is no way in which they can 'buy' food. The only needs of these primitive people are food and the equipment to obtain it, and all of these needs are provided by the environment. This way of life is called a *subsistence economy*. The amount of hunting depends very much on the area inhabited. The *Semang* pygmies of the Malayan jungles are surrounded by a wealth of vegetable food and hunt only small animals such as birds, squirrels and occasionally wild pigs. The Bushmen, however, exist mainly on game – antelope for example – as there is little vegetable food in their Kalahari desert home. The hunting and gathering life imposes a *nomadic* way of life on the people, for if they were to settle in one place they would very soon exhaust the natural resources of the area. As a rule such people live in small family groups (*clans*) each of which seems to have a definite hunting territory. The oldest men are leaders but there are no chiefs or rulers. The Australian Aborigines hunt with spears and throwing sticks, for they have no bows and arrows. This is one of the reasons for believing that these people are the most primitive of all. However they have *boomerangs* which are curved throwing sticks so made that if they miss their target they will curl round and return in the direction of the thrower. The Aborigines also possess *spear-throwers*. These are simple yet very clever devices, found in all spear-throwing communities, for increasing the range of the weapon. A spear-thrower gives extra length and leverage to the arm. The weapons are tipped with flint points or sharply pointed wood. The Bushmen and Semang (among others) use poisonous substances in order to kill their food more quickly. These two groups use bows and arrows as well as spears. In all hunting and gathering communities the men hunt while the

Eskimo woman making fire. By moving the bow to and fro the 'bit' is turned.

women gather the vegetable foods. For carrying the food the women use bags made from naturally occurring fibres, bark and even their own hair. Strips of bark rolled up and tied are used in Australia for carrying small pieces of flint and other objects. The *digging stick* is an important piece of equipment. It is simply a pointed stick about three feet long which is used to dig up juicy roots – often the only source of water. A special stone is frequently used with the stick to give more leverage.

Stone axes and knives are made by fixing sharpened stones into wooden handles with a resinous material. The stone blades resemble those of upper Palaeolithic times. The few clothes that are worn are made from plant fibres, bark or skins. Shelters are also made from these materials. In the case of the Bushmen or the Aborigines a few branches stuck into the ground and covered with leaves or skins make a useful temporary shelter.

Water is a vital commodity to all people. The Bushmen and the Australian natives who both live in dry areas need to store and carry water.

Some aspects of life among the Australian Aborigines. The spear-thrower gives extra range and speed to the spear.

This they do in ostrich egg shells and hollowed-out logs respectively. Fire – which Man has used for the last half a million years – is made in present-day primitive communities in the same manner as it was in the Stone Age. New fires are made by the time-honoured method of rubbing sticks together.

Mesolithic or Middle Stone Age cultures are found among the Eskimos and various groups of Indians on the North West Coast of America. The Eskimos inhabit the barren lands of Northern Canada and Greenland and live almost entirely by hunting. They make well-fitting garments from skins sewn together with sinews. Man could not have inhabited such cold regions until he had invented some sort of needle with which to sew clothes. The Eskimos use bone needles called *burins* for this purpose. They spend the winter hunting seals and fishing in the sea. During the short summer they hunt caribou (American reindeer) and collect what vegetable food they can from the sparse vegetation. Nothing is wasted from the animals they catch. There is little or no wood available and bone serves for making canoes, bows and arrows and most of their tools. Metallic copper is often found in this region and is beaten into shape and used for scraping skins and cutting meat. The people have no knowledge of smelting and are technically still in the Stone Age. Animal skins are used for clothing, tents and for covering the canoes. The Eskimos usually live in larger groups than the hunters and gatherers already described, and the beginnings of social life can be seen.

The North West Coast tribes are near to rich fishing grounds and have given up the nomadic existence. They have villages of permanent wooden houses and quite an elaborate social life. There is no agriculture, however, and the people depend upon the natural resources of their area for vegetable food.

The various horse and reindeer herders of Siberia probably represent the earliest stages of farming development. They are still nomadic to some extent as the herds continually require fresh pastures. The *Nuer* and various other tribes in Africa herd cows and also grow millet (a grain crop). Cattle and grain produce all their requirements but both are very dependent upon the weather and seasons. Most of the African cultivators know how to smelt iron and, although their methods are primitive, they are technically in the Iron Age.

Since Aurignacian times, about fifty thousand years ago, there has been only one species of human animal – *Homo sapiens*. There are, however, various forms or *varieties* of man – compare for instance the short Eskimo and the tall dark African Negro. In spite of these differences, all the varieties are able to mate and to produce normal fertile offspring.

Many attempts have been made to classify the groups of Man. Linnaeus, in the 18th century, proposed four groups which he called *varieties*. They were based on skin coloration and continent. His groups were: the Red Indians of America, the European Whites, the Negroes of Africa and the Asiatic yellow-skinned people. Blumenbach in 1775 emphasised that although these varieties exist, all are linked by intermediates and belong to the single species *Homo sapiens*. This is an important point. Blumenbach himself distinguished five groups of Mankind taking into account head and face shape, form of hair, and colour of skin.

In order to draw up a suitable scheme of classification one must first decide what characters are important in grouping or separating the various types. Cultural differences such as those of language and religion do not express differences in the people themselves. Such features are very much affected by immigration, conquest, etc., and they are of little practical value. It seems therefore that *physical* characters are of greater use in classifying the varieties of Man.

Among these physical characters, colour is the most obvious but it is not diagnostic of any one group. Dark-skinned people occur in various parts of the tropical regions and it is almost certain that dark skin is an adaptation to climatic conditions. Nose-shape has also been put forward as a distinguishing feature but this too is an expression of adaptation to climate. The broad, open nose of the tropical negro would be very unsuitable in cold climates. The narrow nose of the Eskimo ensures that the air is warmed up in the nasal passages before it reaches the lungs. Stature or build is influenced by climate. People of tropical regions tend to be thinner (*i.e.* they have a relatively greater surface through which they can lose heat) than those of colder climates. Diet also influences stature.

One of the most useful features is hair structure. There are three fairly distinct forms: the wavy hair characteristic of Europeans, the coiled 'woolly' hair of negroes and the straight dark hair of the Chinese. Head-shape is another useful character (see illustration). Using the formula given, we can classify men as short-heads, long-heads or medium-heads. However, head-shape too may be influenced by nutrition if changes in stature are produced. It must be remembered that there is much variation of characters within a single group. With the development of blood transfusion much has been learned about the distribution of blood groups, especially of the ABO system. The percentage distribution of the major blood groups affords some clues to the origins and affinities of populations. The value of these blood groups lies in the fact that they do not appear to be influenced by environment.

Using the hair characters mentioned earlier one can recognise three major groups which Dr. J. C. Trevor has called *Europiform*, *Negriform* and *Mongoliform*. There are two other smaller groups which do not fit well into the three major ones. These are the *Khoisaniform* and the *Australiform* groups. By studying other features – especially the shape of the head and face – the major groups can be further divided although the differences at this level are not so clear. Here the term '*race*' is retained for these subdivisions of the major groups.

Europiforms

This group has at present a very wide distribution but much of the spread has occurred very recently in Man's history *e.g.* the colonisation of the Americas by Europeans. Discounting such recent migrations we can say that the Europiforms occupy most of Europe and extend through the Middle East to India. The skin varies from white to dark and all head forms are found. The hair is generally wavy and is well developed on face and body. The nose is narrow. Within this group there are a number of races. Each race has some distinctive features which separate it from neighbouring ones and inhabits a fairly well defined area. Migration and interbreeding have produced a great deal of mixing within the Europiforms but the basic races can still be recognised. The *Nordics* are generally tall, long-headed people characteristic of Britain and Scandinavia. The *Baltics* extend from Finland and Poland eastwards, covering most of European Russia. They are of

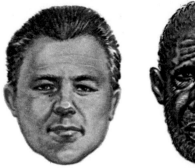

Facial shape is often used to distinguish races. (left) A broad Alpine face and (right) the narrow face of a Papuan.

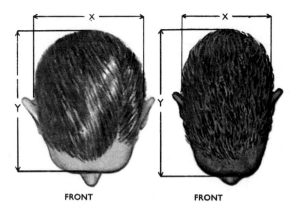

Head shape is an important character. In both figures maximum breadth (X) and maximum length (Y) are shown. $\frac{x}{y} \times 100$ is known as the cephalic index. If this figure is more than 82 the head is short, if under 77, the head is long.

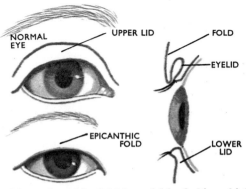

The epicanthic fold is a fold of skin which sometimes hangs over the upper eyelid. It is most common in Mongoliform people.

81

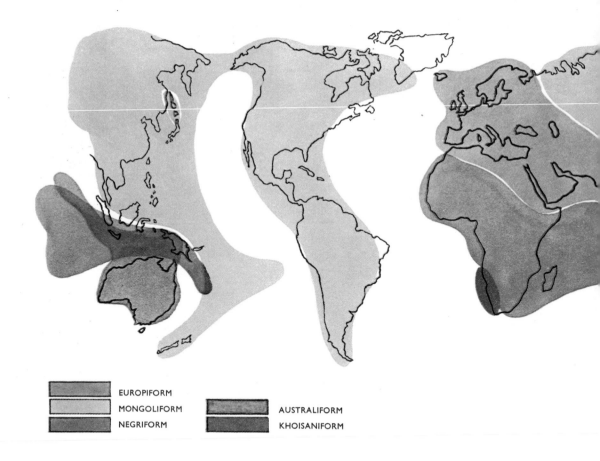

medium build and have short heads. Various Northern groups – notably the *Lapps* – are also Europiform.

The *Alpine* race typically inhabits central Europe from France to Hungary. They are thickset people with short head and broad face. Similar but taller people exist in the Balkan regions, Asia Minor and the Caspian area. The *Mediterranean* race is a mixture itself. The people have long heads and a dusky skin. They extend from Spain and North Africa, along the Mediterranean coasts, through Asia Minor and Persia and into India. The European Mediterraneans are stocky, but going eastward the race tends to become taller and the face more angular. The *Erythriotes* are the inhabitants of North East Africa. They are intermediate in character between Europiforms and Negriforms but apart from their dark skin appear to be closer to the former. The bulk of the Indian population are *Chₒsiotes*. Their head is long and the eyes and hair black. Hair is scarce on the face and body. The skin is dark brown. Other small groups of Europiforms are scattered in Asia *e.g.* the *Ainu* of Japan.

Negriforms

These people are typified by coiled hair, very dark skin and a protruding face (the *prognathous* condition). They also have thick lips and flat noses. The African *Negroes* occupy most of the area south of the Sahara. They are of various shades of brown and

The map shows as far as possible the distribution of the five major divisions of Man apart from recent migration.

have long heads. They are normally slim with long limbs. They include the West African tribes, the *Nilotic* people of the Sudan and most of the Bantu-speaking people in the South and East of the continent, *e.g.* the *Zulu*. The Congo pygmies are called *Negrillos*. They are much shorter and generally lighter coloured than the Negroes. The other Negriform area is in South East Asia where there are several pygmy groups (*e.g.* the *Semang*) called *Negritos*. These usually have short heads but are otherwise similar to African pygmies. The *Papuans* and *Melanesians* of New Guinea and neighbouring islands are dark skinned and have *long* spiralled hair. The Papuans have longer heads than the Melanesians and are less prognathous. This

region is, as can be seen from the map, occupied by at least three of the major groups and there has been much interbreeding.

Mongoliforms

This is the largest ·of the major groups with members over the greater part of Asia and the Pacific. The Eskimos and all the original Indians of the Americas are also Mongoliforms. Chief characteristics are black straight hair, a flat face and yellowish to reddish skin. Hair is very scarce on the body. The head is usually short. A common feature is the *epicanthic fold* (see illustration). The *Mongolian* race comprises most of the inhabitants of Japan, China and Indo China as well as the various ·reindeer-herding people of Siberia. Stature is short to medium. The East Indian region supports a number of types which show affinities with both Europiform and Mongoliform groups. The *Polynesians* of the Pacific Islands and the *Maoris* of New Zealand are of Mongoliform type but they are taller than the typical forms. The *Arctic* race, which includes the Eskimos, are short, thickset people, consistent with their environment. The skin is yellowish brown and the hair dark. The head is long and has a high dome. The face is very broad. There are eight races of American Indians which range from Alaska to Tierra del Fuego. Stature and head shape varies. These people are thought to represent successive migrations from Asia via Alaska. The inhabitants of Tierra del Fuego with a simple hunting and food-gathering economy are regarded as the descendants of the first migrants. The Red Indians of the North American plains would

AUSTRALIAN ABORIGINE

BUSHMAN

NORTH AMERICAN INDIAN

The Melanesians use small canoes for fishing and trading with neighbouring islands.

therefore represent a much later migration. Blood group frequencies are fairly constant among all South American Indians.

In South West Africa there is a small population of dark-skinned people – the Bushmen or **Khoisaniforms.** They live in the semi-desert by hunting and gathering food. The hair is short and tightly coiled – appearing as clumps on the long head. The nose is flat and lips are thick. A peculiar feature is the deposition of fat in the buttocks – a condition called *steatopygia*. The Bushmen are short and lightly built.

The **Australiforms** occur in Australia, Ceylon and some parts of India. Hair is black and wavy and common on the body. The head is long and smaller than in any other group. Prognathism is always present. The Indian and Celanese types (*Veddians*) are possibly taller than the Australians but otherwise the differences are not great. These people are also hunters and gatherers.

The question of origin and primitiveness of groups has often been asked but until the fossil record is more complete we cannot say whether one group is more primitive than another. Probably, Cro-Magnon man, with his superior ability to survive, originated in India or Central Asia and eventually covered the whole world. Over many thousands of years the groups described above gradually developed their own distinct characteristics as interbreeding between them was virtually eliminated by their isolation, due to such factors as oceans, rivers, etc. The dates at which each of the groups became recognisable can only be estimated roughly but it is thought that the Mongolian and Negro races are relatively recent in comparison to the American Indians and the Europiforms. It is also possible that in the future the differences will disappear now that most of these barriers are down.

Agriculture

CHAPTER TEN

The Plough

UNTIL about 7,000 years ago, Man was purely a hunter, living on what food he could catch or gather in the wild. It was not until Neolithic times that Man, began to cultivate the land and grow food instead of going out to look for it. One of the first tools needed was something to turn over the soil and break it up so that crops could be planted. Simple sticks were used at first but, gradually, more complicated tools were developed, culminating in the modern plough.

At first sight the plough is a simple tool, no more important than a dozen implements used by the farmer in his everyday work. Indeed, the fundamental role played by the plough is only recognised if we consider what we should do without it. Whole fields would have to be dug over with spade and fork or by the most primitive and inefficient digging tools, with an enormous expenditure of labour. The principal advantage of the plough is that it enables the mechanical force of the tractor or the horse to be employed to speed up the preparation of the land and to cut down the amount of human effort. Like most such labour-saving devices, however, it is at its most efficient when

a large amount of straightforward work has to be done. There would be little point, for example, in using a tractor-drawn plough in a small back garden, but in a large open field the advantages soon become evident.

What exactly does a plough do? Its main object is to turn over the surface of the soil. The principle is quite simple. The iron *plough share* (see illustration) makes a horizontal cut a few inches below the surface of the soil as the implement is pulled along. Another cutting edge, the *coulter*, cuts vertically into the soil so that a long ribbon of soil is cut out. The *mouldboard* of the plough, behind the share, is twisted and turns the ribbon of soil to one side with the result that the side which was originally below ground is now uppermost. The ribbon is not usually turned over completely, however, but left at a slant, producing the characteristic furrows and ridges we know so well.

This is the basic principle of the plough, but there are many important refinements. The depth of the furrows being cut, for example, can be adjusted by altering the height of the *furrow wheel* and the *land wheel* (the former is larger than the latter since

The range of trailed ploughs may vary from a single-furrow deep-digging type to six-furrow types that are ideal for use on large areas where mounted ploughs might prove less economical.

FURROW WHEEL   FURROW WHEEL   LAND WHEEL

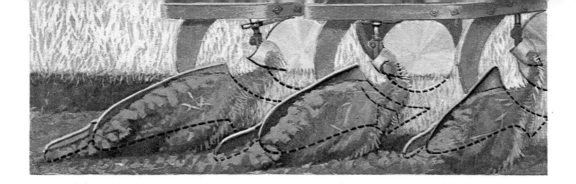

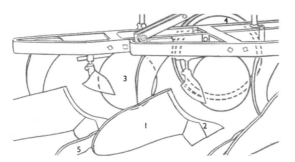

1. MOULDBOARD
2. SHARE
3. COULTER DISC
4. LAND WHEEL
5. TAILPIECE

(Above) A diagram showing how the parts of the plough operate in cutting a ribbon of soil and turning it over.

it runs along a furrow previously cut, while the land wheel rests on the higher, unploughed earth). Another important feature is the device by which the plough share can be lifted from the soil surface so that no furrows are made as the plough turns round at the end of the field (the 'headland').

The advent of the powerful tractor made it easier to produce several furrows at the same time, by using two, three or more plough shares and their related equipment set together. This obviously makes for a great saving in time and labour. The shares are set diagonally, to allow space for the soil behind each share to be turned over cleanly.

The main purpose of ploughing is to turn over the soil to bury the weeds and the remains of previous crops so that when new seed is planted it will have good conditions in which to grow. There are, however, several

other important results. Ploughing allows air to get at the soil and prevents it from becoming water-logged. It 'digs in' the surface vege-table matter so that it can decay to form valuable humus (a rich source of plant food).

The type of soil greatly affects the depth at which the plough share cuts, as does the kind of crop to be grown. Generally speaking the depth of cut varies between 4 inches and a foot, though some special ploughs are capable of cutting twice as deep as this. There are of course several differ-ent kinds of ploughs, adapted for special purposes. *Lea* ploughs are sometimes used for autumn ploughing and have a long mouldboard, produc-ing a continuous furrow which is broken up during the winter frosts. *Digger* ploughs have a shorter mould-board, giving a broken furrow more suitable for the planting of crops.

A mounted plough in use. Mounted ploughs have several advantages over trailed ploughs (*page 86*). The depth of ploughing can be automatically adjusted and the weight of the plough can be released from the rear wheels of the tractor if an obstruction is encountered, thereby avoiding damage. They are usually lifted in and out of work hydraulically. The hydraulic system is operated by the tractor driver, and most modern farm tractors are so fitted. (Below) Three types of plough body suitable for different purposes: (a) general purpose – ideal for grassland; (b) semi-digging – partly breaks up the soil; (c) digging – suitable for deep ploughing, furrow slice broken.

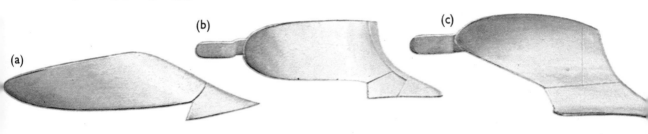

CHAPTER ELEVEN

Irrigation

THE development of the plough meant that many previously un-cultivated lands could be brought into use but, however useful it is, the plough cannot make dry desert land suitable for crops. Plants all need a certain amount of water for growth and will not grow unless water is available.

Many regions of the world are now artificially supplied with water so that crops can be grown. Such artificial watering is called irrigation – from the Latin word *rigare*, meaning to carry water. Irrigation is usually necessary in tropical and sub-tropical regions where the rainfall is less than 20 inches per year. In cooler regions, the rain-fall does not evaporate so quickly and irrigation is not usually necessary.

In some regions irrigation may only be needed during part of the year (the hot season), whilst in other areas, such as Egypt, crops depend almost entirely upon artificially supplied water. Irrigation is also necessary where the rainfall, though sufficient, is unreliable. Great famines have occurred in such regions through farmers 'trusting to providence'. The importance of irrigation may be seen in the fact that fully half of the world's cultivated land is irrigated to a certain extent.

Irrigation may also depend upon the crop grown. Rice, for instance, which spends part of its growing period under about six inches of water, needs additional water where another, less thirsty plant would grow quite happily. A considerable amount of rice is grown in South East Asia by trapping the large amounts of rain-water brought by the monsoon—hence the small, level, rimmed fields which turn whole hillsides into a gigantic flight of 'water steps'.

The idea of irrigation is not new: in Egypt crops have always depended almost entirely upon the River Nile for water. The ancient Egyptians utilised the fact that the Nile floods once per year. They developed a system of canals and ditches to carry the floodwaters through the fields, a practice which would be known today as flood irrigation. For the rest of the year they depended upon primitive devices to raise water from the river to the level of the channels.

Large-scale, efficient irrigation schemes can only be operated when these inundation canals (canals which fill with water only in time of flood) and other primitive devices have been replaced by perennial canals (those which carry water the whole year round), a process that is rapidly taking place. But perennial canals are costly, for they entail the dam-ming of rivers to control floodwaters and create artificial reservoirs which can be drawn upon at all times of the year.

In Egypt the volume of the River Nile from August to November greatly exceeds the demands made upon it by irrigation, while for the rest of the year the natural flow cannot meet the farmers' needs. At the beginning of this century a dam was built at Aswan to control the floodwater and save some of

it for the rest of the year. The dam has been raised twice since but it still lets an enormous amount of valuable water escape to the sea. The Aswan High Dam is the latest scheme to make full use of the river's possibilities. Behind it will form one of the world's largest artificial lakes, 15,000 square miles in area.

The Aswan High Dam is typical of most dam projects in tropical lands. It combines flood control and the production of electricity with the storage of water for irrigation. Apart from providing water to increase the irrigated land by 30%, the Aswan High Dam will eventually produce six times the amount of electricity used in the whole of Egypt at present.

Although irrigation is often connected with Egypt, it is India and Pakistan which have the most extensive systems. In fact one great irrigation scheme, based upon the Sukkur barrage across the River Indus, changed a barren area larger than the total amount of Egypt's irrigated land into fertile farmland.

One of the boldest irrigation schemes of modern times is the Snowy Mountains project in south-eastern Australia. The aim is to impound the waters of the Snowy River, which flows through a region of adequate rainfall, and lead it back *through* the mountains, largely by pipes, to augment the waters of the Murray and Murrumbidgee Rivers for inland irrigation. The plan calls for the construction of nine big dams, more than 100 miles of aqueducts and at least ten big power stations, some of them underground.

Simplified plan of the Snowy Mountains project.

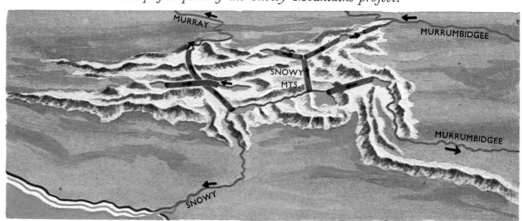

CHAPTER TWELVE

Land Drainage

CROPS will not grow without water but they can have too much water and drainage of the land is as important for farmers in some regions as irrigation is in others.

Low-lying areas and hollows, especially those along river valleys, are frequently flooded after only a moderate rainfall. The fields (*water meadows*), even when they are not covered with water, do not support much more than grass and such marsh-loving plants as rushes and kingcups (*Marsh Marigolds*). This is because the soil is waterlogged, i.e. the spaces between the soil particles are filled with water instead of air. Plant roots need oxygen in order to grow and ordinary plants cannot survive in waterlogged soil. The typical marsh plants have in their roots a system of passages and spongy tissue which enables oxygen to reach all parts of the root. Many micro-organisms, present in normal soil, are missing from waterlogged soil because of the lack of oxygen. They play an essential part in the decay of humus; without them, an acid condition is built up which is not suitable for most plants.

Waterlogging is the result of certain conditions in the underlying rocks, although low-lying regions may be temporarily flooded by water running off from the surrounding hills after heavy rains. When rain falls on to dry soil it is rapidly soaked up, the water being held on the surface of the soil particles. Further rain is soaked up until the soil particles are completely covered with a film of water. Any more water runs down through the soil under the influence of gravity until it reaches an impermeable rock (i.e. one which prevents penetration of water). Clays will not let water pass through them. As the water cannot penetrate any more it builds up gradually and forces air out of the soil spaces. This water is called ground water and its surface is called the water table. If the impermeable rock is near to the soil surface the water table may rise above the soil and create flooding.

Water draining through the chalk is forced out at springs along the line X——X. By digging a ditch along the spring line the water can be conveyed to the stream without waterlogging the surrounding soil.

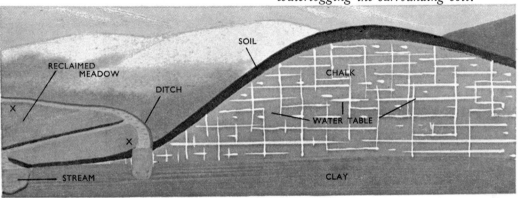

Pipe drains being laid in a narrow channel excavated by a tractor-drawn machine. The pipes are unglazed so that water can pass into them.

If the land slopes, the surface water will run off and the ground water will gradually drain away through the soil layers until it reaches a stream, but low-lying flat land will not drain quickly enough to be of use to the farmer.

When the clay is a long way down, waterlogging will be rare as the water table will seldom reach the soil surface. If the clay is at the surface there will be no penetration of water and a pond will be formed in any slight hollow. Waterlogging may also be caused by continuous seepage from *springs*. If, on its passage through the ground, water meets a very porous rock such as sandstone or limestone, it will move along the rock as well as vertically downwards. When the water reaches the edge of the porous rock it will run out at a series of springs. If a spring occurs on a steep slope it may give rise to a stream, but on flatter ground a marsh will develop if there is an impermeable rock below the surface.

Since much of the soil of river valleys is rich in mineral plant foods the farmer cannot afford to let it remain as unworkable marshland. The value of draining land has been known ever since agriculture has been practised. Its purpose is to convey surface and ground water away quickly and to ensure that the water table does not rise above the lower limit of root growth. Flooding due to run-off or stream overflow may be dealt with by *open drains*. These are ditches cut through the fields in order to carry the water to a lower level and into the stream again more quickly than would occur by natural drainage. Open drainage schemes have been used on a large scale for draining the Fens of England and large areas of Holland.

Although the open drain system is easy to keep clear it is not suitable for highly cultivated land as the ditches would hinder ploughing and other operations. Open drains are used on forested lands.

Under Drainage

When agricultural land requires drainage of ground water a system of underground drains is usually employed. These may be *pipe* or *mole* drains. The pipe drains, as their name suggests, consist of a network of pipes placed at a certain depth under the surface. They are made of unglazed tile so that ground water will seep into them quite rapidly and be carried away. Thus the water table will not rise above the level of the drains. If an area is to be drained it must first be *surveyed*, i.e. the highest and lowest points must be determined together with the directions of the slopes. A plan can then be drawn up before the work is started. The steepest slopes are drained by a series of small parallel pipes (minor drains) running obliquely. The minor pipes join larger 'mains' running along the shallower, lower slopes to the outlet at the stream or ditch. Great care is taken to ensure that the *fall* (i.e. the slope) of the drain is regular, but it must not be too steep or the running water may damage the pipes. Mechanical ditchers are normally used to make the excavations. They can dig a regularly sloping channel regardless of slight ridges on the surface. The pipes are carefully laid so that there are no gaps through which soil can pass and possibly block the drain. On flat ground the channels are dug so that they get deeper towards the outlet. The pipes must be at a sufficient depth so that the normal ploughing operations will not disturb them. In light soil three to four feet is a very suitable depth. A heavy soil in which drainage is slow requires shallower drains—not more than 24 inches from the surface. The character of the soil determines the distance between drains too. Twenty-four feet is a maximum in heavy soil, but drains 90 feet apart may be adequate for light soil.

Pipe drainage is very costly and is economical only where valuable, permanent crops (e.g. vines) are being grown on the land, or where other types of drainage are not practical. *Mole drainage* is such an alternative and is comparatively cheap. The minor drains are not tiled. They are channels formed by hauling a bullet-shaped piece of metal (the *mole*) about 3 inches in diameter through the sub-soil. The mole is attached to an arm behind a powerful tractor. It cannot automatically allow for large surface irregularities and is only suitable

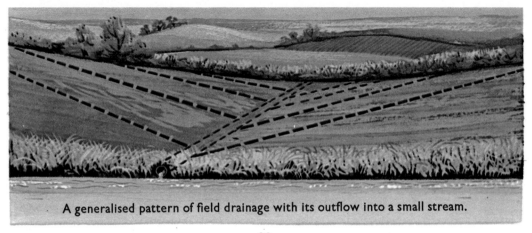

A generalised pattern of field drainage with its outflow into a small stream.

93

therefore when there is a steady fall of the land. As there are no pipes the walls of the mole drains collapse after a time and the field needs to be mole-ploughed again. Mole drains are between twenty and thirty inches deep to avoid possible collapse due to the pressure of tractors or other surface disturbances. Mole drains are not so efficient as pipe drains and need to be closer together. They empty into piped main drains which are laid down in the usual way.

Where waterlogging is due to eruption of springs large open drains are again used. Deep channels, cut along the edge of the porous rock, convey the spring water into the nearest stream and waterlogging of the land is avoided.

A powerful tractor is required to haul the mole through the heavy soil.

CHAPTER THIRTEEN

Composting

IN a natural community, leaves and other organic materials fall to the ground and rot so that their *constituent* minerals are returned to the soil for the use of a further generation of plants. When Man grows crops he takes most of the material (sometimes all of it) so that little remains to be returned to the soil. In order to grow good crops year after year, Man must return to the soil the goodness taken out by his crops. He does this by adding fertilizers, manure, or compost.

The art of composting is one that has been known to Man for many years. For example, in Japan and China intensive cultivation has been achieved for at least four thousand years, largely by the intelligent and wide use of compost.

Compost is strictly a mixture of various kinds of animal and vegetable waste material, though nowadays attempts are being made to compost numerous other wastes. Household refuse, for example, minus tins and other metallic material, is pulverised, sifted, wetted and then aerated by stirring. Bacteria are added, to augment the actions of the normal population of micro-organisms, and the harmful substances in the waste are broken down chemically. The digested matter (compost) is dried and bagged. Enriching substances such as phosphate, nitrate and so on may be added prior to bagging.

The main aim of composting is to produce *humus*. This consists of the broken down remains and wastes of animals and plants – the so-called *soil organic matter*. Worms, insects, larger animals and their droppings, dead leaves and branches, and myriads of bacteria, fungi, protozoans, and algae all contribute to the humus. It consists of substances in various stages of decay, and contains fluctuating populations of living organisms.

Of great importance in the making of humus are earthworms. They eat their way through the soil, allowing air to enter and turning the soil over. They drag plant material down into their burrows, bringing it into contact with the teeming soil population. The actions of weather and the millions of living soil inhabitants convert the dead and decaying plants and animals into the familiar 'earthy mould' that is mature humus; a material rich in protein and other organic molecules and various kinds of minerals.

Good soil should contain adequate amounts of humus, for its presence provides several essential requirements for plant growth. It is the

Nowadays compost can be spread rapidly by mechanical means.

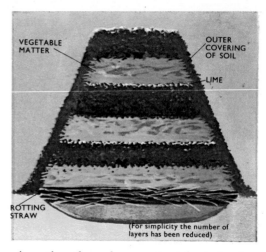

VEGETABLE MATTER

OUTER COVERING OF SOIL

LIME

ROTTING STRAW

(For simplicity the number of layers has been reduced)

A section through a compost heap to show the shape and the arrangement of the various layers.

medium in which many chemical and biological changes take place. It is a rich store of plant foods, and nutrients 'locked up' in it are not readily leached out of the soil by rain. The presence of humus promotes the uptake (by the plant) of substances such as sulphate, phosphate, nitrate and iron. It darkens light-coloured soils, and as a result they become warmer through absorbing a greater proportion of the sun's rays. Humus also gives the soil a crumbly texture, binding light sandy particles together and helping it to retain water, and yet reducing the stickiness of clay, improving its drainage and air supply.

These 'qualities' of humus make it one of the principal agents in combating erosion. Overcropping and the consequent exhaustion of the soil humus content dries up the soil, encourages water to run off and thus enhances the action of wind and rain. Man-made dustbowls, such as that in Kansas, U.S.A., show the necessity for maintaining a sufficient quantity of humus.

The art of composting is to stimulate the natural production of humus in the soil – achieving the right balance of wastes and soil and providing the conditions that promote their rapid decomposition by micro-organisms.

Composting is a valuable means of changing what would often be an offensive mass of otherwise waste materials into something that will act both as a manure and as a soil improver. Generally it is more efficient to apply well rotted compost to the soil than to turn raw plant and animal waste directly into the soil.

Compost contains many substances that green plants and soil micro-organisms require as food. These include nitrogen, phosphorus, potassium, calcium, iron, magnesium and silicon, together with trace elements such as manganese, boron, cobalt and zinc. The proportions of these constituents vary with the waste materials used and with the method of composting.

Research has shown clearly that there are considerable differences between a compost heap that is sodden and poorly aerated and one that is moist and has a good air supply. Different micro-organisms thrive in each instance. In the former case the only microbes that grow and reproduce are those that are able to utilise the chemicals in the compost when free oxygen is absent or when it is present in minute quantities. They are said to be *anaerobic*. *Aerobic* organisms can grow and multiply rapidly only when abundant supplies of air are available. A moist, well aerated heap satisfies these requirements. Moulds and heat-loving (thermophilic) bacteria thrive in such conditions, fixing nitrogen and producing large quantities of heat so that the temperature of the compost heap rises. In a well-made compost heap temperatures of 150°–160°F are produced. At these temperatures disease-causing bacteria are killed, the eggs, larvae and pupae of flies are killed and so the latter cannot breed. Heat also kills weed seeds. If a compost heap is not well drained and aerated, however, little heat is generated by the anaerobic microbes and so pathogens (disease-causing bacteria) will multiply and flies and other pests are provided with ideal facilities for breeding. Such heaps often release unpleasant smells and they lose their nutrients (particularly nitrogen) very rapidly.

Obviously then, the aim is to produce a moist but well drained and well aerated compost heap. The siting of the heap and its construction is of the greatest importance, therefore. To provide the most favourable conditions for micro-organisms, earthworms etc., the site should be chosen where the drying effects of sun and wind are at a minimum and, at the same time, to avoid excessive rain and the drippings from trees. Rain and drippings may cause waterlogging and

leaching of chemicals from the heap.

Many wastes may be used to make a compost heap. Those from the house include egg shells, tea leaves, carpet sweepings, rags, and dead flowers. Lawn cuttings, bonfire ash, weeds, straw and hay refuse, animal and bird manures, are wastes from farm or garden. Many other wastes may be added too, such as hedge-cuttings, wood-shavings and sawdust, grain husks, and various bagged organic manures (e.g. treated sewage) and minerals such as lime. The latter is an important additive which prevents the heap from becoming too acid and also helps to destroy weed-seeds.

All waste materials added to the heap should be moist. They should be arranged in layers on top of the foundations with thin layers of soil containing lime in between. Animal manure helps speed up decay and is valuable next to vegetable remains. As the heap is built up it should be sloped inwards to form a flat ridge. A final covering of peat or moss is needed with an outer layer of soil. This forms a heat-retaining 'skin'.

Overcropping reduces the humus content of the soil until plant growth is reduced to such a low level that there are too few roots to bind the soil particles together. It crumbles and is easily eroded away by wind and water.

CHAPTER FOURTEEN

Fertilizers

FOR several thousand years man has added manure and compost to the soil in order to grow healthy crops and to increase the yield. But it is only in recent years that our knowledge of plant chemistry has been sufficient for us to understand what makes a plant grow – and, therefore, why manuring is beneficial.

A plant consists mainly of the elements carbon, oxygen, hydrogen and nitrogen. Most of the carbon and oxygen is obtained from carbon dioxide in the atmosphere and nearly all the hydrogen is obtained from water absorbed by the roots. Nitrogen is taken in through the roots mainly as nitrate dissolved in the soil water. Analysis of plant ash shows that the plant also contains several other elements, namely iron, magnesium, alu-minium, calcium, potassium, sodium, silicon, phosphorus, sulphur, and chlorine. Not all of these appear to be essential for the healthy growth of a plant. For example the omission of sodium and chlorine from water cultures has no apparent harmful effect.

Besides the elements already mentioned, plants also need minute amounts of boron, molybdenum, manganese, zinc and copper. These are known as the *trace elements*.

Scientists are gradually finding out what roles these various elements have in the life of the plant. For instance, while certain minimum quantities must be present in the soil, too great a quantity may also be harmful so that the application of artificial dressings to the soil must be carefully balanced.

Granular fertilizer being distributed by a spinning disc type of spreader.

The amount of available farmyard manure is only a fraction of the total required to maintain crop yields at their present level and, to maintain the proper level of soil organic matter, it must be supplemented by the use of *fertilizers*. The chemists of the nineteenth century deduced that a small quantity of fertilizer supplies the amount of plant food present in a ton of farmyard manure. So they started to look for mineral salts that contain the elements needed by plants. Chile saltpetre (sodium nitrate) had been used for some time, as had ammonium sulphate. The former occurs in vast deposits in Chile, and sulphate of ammonia was becoming available in larger quantities as a by-product of the coal gas industry which was expanding rapidly.

However, the fertilizer industry was really established after John Lawes, an English landowner, discovered that bone dissolved in sulphuric acid had a beneficial effect on plant growth. Bone is rich in calcium phosphate and at the time large quantities of this chemical were found in Germany. In 1842 Lawes set up a factory for the production of treated calcium phosphate or *superphosphate* as it was called.

For many years superphosphate was the only fertilizer manufactured, but the present century has seen the development of a bewildering range of artificial plant foods. Besides these inorganic plant foods, organic fertilizers have been developed. The application of these, together with the practice of ploughing-in green crops and straw, helps to maintain a sufficient level of soil organic matter. Due to their high cost of manufacture, organics are almost exclusively used in horticulture, especially by market gardeners.

Fertilizers are of two main types, *organic*, that is, derived from animal and plant residues or waste products, and *inorganic*. Inorganic fertilizers may be synthetic (e.g. sulphate of ammonia) or 'natural', e.g. potash, which is used in the same form as it is mined. Superphosphate, is an example of a fertilizer formed by chemical treatment of a naturally occurring mineral (phosphate rock). Some organic fertilizers (e.g. Dried Blood) supply only nitrogen (12–15%) while others supply nitrogen and phosphate (e.g. Bone Meal – about 4% N, 22% insoluble P_2O_5). The same applies to inorganic fertilizers. Sulphate of Ammonia supplies nitrogen only (20·8%), and Nitrate of Potash supplies both nitrogen and potassium. (15% N, 10% K_2O). 'Rock Phosphate' and superphosphate supply phosphate only, respectively 27% – 33% P_2O_5 and 16% – 20% P_2O_5), though the former is insoluble and the latter soluble in water. Sulphate of potash supplies potassium only (48% K_2O).

Nowadays many compound fertilizers are sold. These supply several 'single' fertilizers thoroughly mixed together and blended in known quantities. The use of compound fertilizers avoids the separate application of single fertilizers, a great saving in time and money.

Most fertilizers are available in a granular form as well as powder. The granular condition is essential for even distribution.

Fertilizers are essential for maximum crop production. They are not substitutes for farmyard manure or compost but should be used in conjunction with the latter. Most soils have a natural reserve of plant nutrients but adequate amounts of these

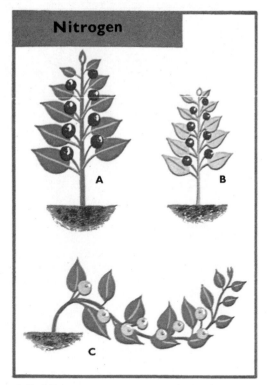

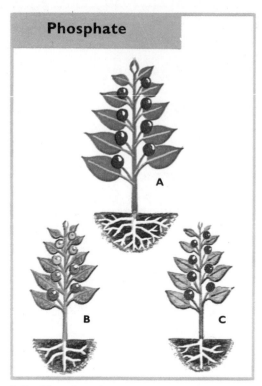

(A) *Nitrogen encourages rapid leaf growth.* (B) *Insufficient nitrogen means poor, weak growth.* (C) *Excessive nitrogen can cause soft rank growth.*

(A) *Phosphate is essential for root development and early maturity.* (B) *Growth is slow and restricted without sufficient phosphate.* (C) *Massive phosphate dressings can induce early ripening.*

are rarely present. Fertilizers supplement the natural supply. Nitrogen, phosphorus and potassium are the most likely to be exhausted quickly from the soil. The modern practice is to apply fertilizer dressings that contain these three essential plant foods in properly balanced amounts. A soil so supplied, and also provided with humus and lime, will satisfy the main requirements of the crops. The continued application of one plant food only is not sufficient, and the yields will become lower and lower.

Nitrogen increases the green colour of leaves, their size, rate of growth and final yields. It is the main plant food for leafy crops such as cereals and greenstuffs. Application to grassland

in the correct quantities promotes lush growth and extends the grazing season. However, excessive application of fertilizers rich in nitrogen may cause overgrowth of the plants which are then particularly susceptible to disease.

Fertilizers containing phosphorus, stimulate root development and are particularly effective on heavy soils. Phosphorus is essential for normal photosynthesis and respiration in the plant. Along with nitrogen, it encourages the development of root nodules on peas, clover and other leguminous crops. By inducing the early ripening of a crop, especially cereals, it enables good harvests to be obtained in wet areas

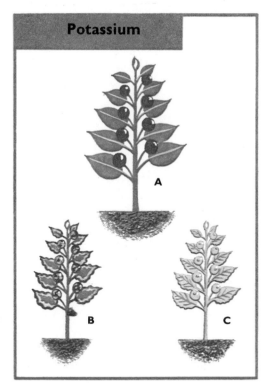

Potassium

(A) *Potassium encourages healthy growth and increases resistance to drought, disease and extremes of temperature.* (B) *With too little potash, leaves may be scorched and plants stunted and disease prone.* (C) *Large unbalanced potash dressings upset mineral nutrition.*

and reduces the chance of the crop being spoiled by the weather. Usually phosphate fertilizers are applied to the soil when the seeds are drilled. The latter thus have a readily available supply of phosphorus from the time that they start to germinate.

Potassium encourages healthy plant growth. It plays an important part in the uptake and utilisation of water, increasing a crop's resistance to drought and reducing the effect of extremes of temperature. It is also concerned with the manufacture of sugars and starch so that its application, as potash, to crops such as potatoes, peas, beans and tomatoes, is particularly effective. Potassium-containing fertilizers dissolve readily in water, but the potash is held by the soil particles and leaching occurs only in very light, sandy soil. Light sandy and chalky soils are the most likely to be deficient as they have no natural potash reserve. Excessive application of potassium fertilizers on their own must be avoided, for this may accentuate abnormalities caused by magnesium deficiency.

Because the requirements of different soils and the needs of different plants vary, a number of fertilizers of widely differing chemical composition are available. The gardener and farmer must be able to see at a glance what each contains. A convenient method of expressing the plant food value of a fertilizer is in terms of Nitrogen (N), Phosphoric acid (P_2O_5) and Potash (K_2O). By law, each fertilizer sold must have a guarantee of its plant food value expressed in terms of N, P_2O_5 and K_2O. Thus sulphate of ammonia is sold as containing $20 \cdot 8\%$ nitrogen (ammonium, NH_4, contains nitrogen) and nitrate of soda contains 16% nitrogen.

The combine drill places the fertilizer close to the seed.

CHAPTER FIFTEEN

Plant Breeding

WITH a small brush Gregor Mendel transferred pollen from a tall garden pea flower to the stigma of a short-stemmed variety. He planted the seeds that were produced and patiently waited to see what height the stems of the new plants would grow to. The year was 1857. Mendel, an Austrian monk, had begun a series of experiments that were to explain the nature of inheritance – the relationship between parents and the offspring they produce.

One of Mendel's most important discoveries was that each character of a plant – the colour of the flowers, the height of the stems – is controlled by what he called 'factors'. (Today they are called *genes*.) When a pollen grain fertilizes an ovule the 'factors', one complete set from each parent plant, are passed on to the next generation. The similarities between the offspring and each of its parents depend upon which of the inherited factors control development.

Man had been unconsciously applying the laws of inheritance long before Mendel's time. Using the principle that 'like breeds like' he had, for instance, bred his domestic animals for the qualities he most desired. Similarly with agricultural plants he has exerted his influence.

By automatically choosing the seeds of the most productive and successful plants he has perpetuated favourable qualities. Hundreds of years of artificial selection have altered our agricultural crops to such an extent that today it is usually difficult to trace them to their original wild ancestors.

In 1719 Man first attempted to control the fertilization of his plants. Pollen was artificially transferred from one carnation to another. The field of plant breeding had become extended. Here was a means of improving crops other than merely selecting the most suitable seeds. Artificial crossing of the genes (or *hybridization*) meant that different characters possessed by closely related varieties could be combined. And this is just what the plant breeders were attempting to do in the late 18th and early 19th centuries.

Today's plant breeders continue this work. Basically the processes used are the same as 200 years ago. Plants are selected and crossed by simply transferring pollen from one to another. But what has changed is the knowledge behind the hybridizations. The work of Mendel and other investigators in explaining the mechanisms of inheritance, has introduced greater surety about what can and cannot be achieved. Cross-breeding is no longer just an outside gamble. From the different varieties of a plant the breeder selects those with favourable qualities. He attempts to combine together the genes which are responsible for these qualities into one plant – usually with a fair degree of certainty.

Aims of the Plant Breeder

What are the aims of the plant breeder? He could of course, by selection and hybridization, breed for all sorts of qualities, bizarre petal formations for instance, and unusual colours of flowers. But a far more important task is improving the productivity of the world's crops.

There are many approaches to this problem. Basically the breeder wants to provide varieties of plants that will ensure agricultural land is most economically used. The yield of a crop can be increased directly, for example by breeding wheat which will provide the maximum weight of grain per ear. But also important are such factors as resistance to disease and pests, hardiness, drought resistance, length of ripening time and in the case of cereal crops the quality and strength of the straw.

It is no good having a variety of wheat which will produce large quantities of grain only in ideal conditions. Strong susceptibility to disease or pests could make the crop valueless; similarly, weak stalks would mean that the wheat is flattened by the first strong wind or torrent of rain. The breeder must compromise. Taking into account the climatic factors of the region, the soil and the diseases and pests, he must provide a crop which will

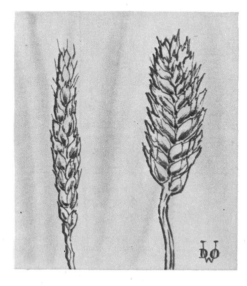

Varieties of wheat produced by artificial mutation. Both natural and artificially produced varieties of a plant are used for breeding.

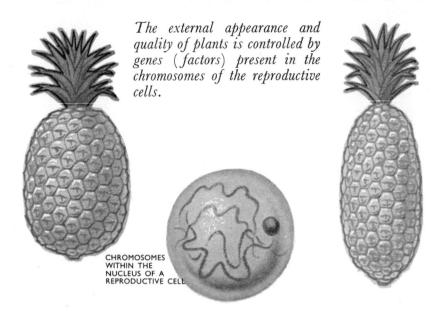

The external appearance and quality of plants is controlled by genes (factors) present in the chromosomes of the reproductive cells.

CHROMOSOMES
WITHIN THE
NUCLEUS OF A
REPRODUCTIVE CELL

produce well under the natural hazards likely to occur. He must manipulate the favourable genes of different varieties until he produces a plant with all the right characters.

Sometimes the necessary qualities are not noticeable in the outside appearance of the plant. An instance is the malting ability of barley, which depends upon the biochemical activities of the plant. Whether a potato will be suitable for making potato crisps is another character not predictable from mere inspection. The breeder here has to analyse the composition of the plants and tries to establish just what chemicals are responsible for the properties he needs to perpetuate.

One other factor the breeder must allow for is the different farming methods that come into use. For instance modern methods of combine-harvesting operate best with cereals having relatively short stalks. The plant breeder has to see that, amongst other properties, his variety possesses the necessary genes for correct length of stalk.

Operations in Plant Breeding

Long years of work face the plant breeder. The development of a new variety of plant takes at the minimum 10 years and usually a lot longer. For this reason the problems undertaken must be important ones. The solutions must offer prospects of real advancement in crop growing.

When presented with a problem the plant breeder first ensures that breeding is the correct answer – that poor crops are not just the reflections of mineral deficiencies in the soil. Then he must look into the genetical make-up of the plants with which he is working. The desired characters, whether for increased size or disease resistance, must not only be controlled by genes but they must be characters **that are identifiable and measurable so that progress in the breeding experiments can be assessed.**

Increasing the productivity of a plant by giving it some additional desirable character means that a closely related plant must be found that already possesses the desirable character. The genes responsible for controlling this character must then be incorporated into the first variety. At the same time any undesirable characters likely to reduce the productivity must be excluded.

The actual crossing or hybridization of the plants is a simple task and requires only a pair of forceps and a brush for transferring the pollen. But some plants, most cereals for example, are naturally self-fertilizing – that is pollen produced by one individual fertilizes the ovules of the same flower. To prevent this from happening, the pollen-producing anthers can be removed at an early stage of their development.

Both in self-pollinating and cross-

Mutations

New variations are constantly occurring in plants. They are caused by mutations – small changes affecting the *chromosomes* (structures which carry the genes) in the nucleus of reproductive cells. Usually those mutations which are advantageous to the plant in its natural surroundings will be passed on to descendants. If the mutation is disadvantageous, the plant, in competition with other plants, may not survive to reproduce.

In different surroundings the successful mutations will also be different and so a number of varieties of one type of plant may come into existence. It is from these varieties that different favourable qualities can be selected.

Today plant breeders also are able to stimulate mutations in plants. Using radioactivity or applying certain chemical compounds, offspring from parent plants can be made to display a variety of different characters. Most will be unfavourable but there is just the possibility that one will be valuable

Disease Resistance

The most prominent diseases attacking crops vary in different parts of a country, and plant breeders bear these regional problems in mind. Within a region however variation in weather from year to year will determine just what type of disease will prosper. Accurate weather forecasting on such a scale is not possible at present. If it is difficult to breed plants with high resistance to all likely diseases in an area, there is a possible alternative. Seed can be mixed; varieties of a plant can be sown together differing in their resistances to the different diseases. Whatever disease attacks, only a part of the crop will be susceptible and as the susceptible plants are likely to be surrounded by resistant plants a large scale outbreak is prevented.

Another problem is that the organisms responsible for disease (the *pathogens*) can change – a crop previously showing strong resistance may be susceptible to the new form. Plant breeders cannot predict the changes. They can only keep a constant watch for the appearance of a new form and attempt to counter the threat before large scale damage is caused.

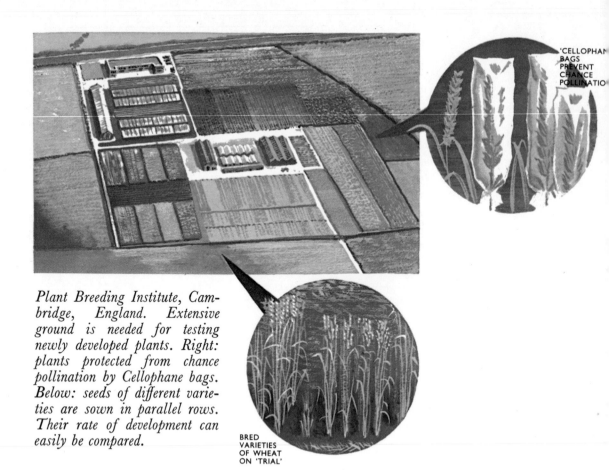

'CELLOPHANE BAGS PREVENT CHANCE POLLINATION'

Plant Breeding Institute, Cambridge, England. Extensive ground is needed for testing newly developed plants. Right: plants protected from chance pollination by Cellophane bags. Below: seeds of different varieties are sown in parallel rows. Their rate of development can easily be compared.

BRED VARIETIES OF WHEAT ON 'TRIAL'

pollinating plants there is always a chance that flowers will be fertilized by stray pollen blown about in the air. So Cellophane bags are tied firmly over the flowers.

The seeds produced from artificial pollination are planted and the offspring examined. Many of the offspring will be no good at all. But just one or two might possess something approaching the correct combinations of genes, and these are kept for further breeding.

Plant breeding establishments need a large acreage of ground for testing the plants they have bred. The plants are sown and their appearance and activities compared with those of their parents and those of other varieties. The different varieties are planted close together so that as far as possible the composition of the soil is the same for all of them. Changes in the properties of the plants then reflect different genetic constitutions and not different conditions of growth. The breeding establishments are also equipped with greenhouses, freezing apparatus and controlled growth rooms so that plants can be tested under all sorts of conditions.

CHAPTER SIXTEEN

Grafting and Budding

IF you enjoy the flavour of a particular variety of apple, you may plant the pips in order to grow the variety yourself. It will, however, be some years before the tree bears any fruit and even then you will be unlikely to get apples tasting quite like the original one. This is because, in the process of seed formation, the characteristics of the parents are mixed up. Nature intended offspring to differ slightly from their parents, not to be all alike.

Obviously, professional growers cannot rely upon this sort of propagation. They must be able to increase their stocks rapidly and they must be able to reproduce a given variety exactly. They rely on *vegetative* methods of propagation which with trees and shrubs usually means *grafting* or *budding*.

These techniques involve joining a shoot or bud (*scion*) of the desired variety onto the stem of another (the *stock*). The tissues must unite completely into a complete plant of which the stock provides the root system whereas the scion produces the branches, flowers and fruit. The vital thing is that the *cambium* of each plant is in contact. This is the ring of living cells just under the bark and only these cells can grow and produce the new cells that knit the scion and stock together. This happens quickly: water and nutrients from the stock pass into the scion and it grows quite happily.

Although the grafted plant grows as a complete individual, the original stock and scion retain their individual characteristics. Shoots (*suckers*) from the stock are of no use and should be removed at once. The stock chosen must be healthy and vigorous and must, in general, be closely related to the scion. It must also be cheap and readily available. Roses are frequently budded onto wild briars and cherry varieties onto stocks of wild cherry. Several types of apple stock are available for grafting. Some New Zealand varieties are resistant to Woolly Aphid and to some virus diseases and they actually pass on the resistance to the scion.

Saddle-grafting — in which a scion is notched to fit on a pointed stock and then bound up until the graft has taken.

Whip-and-tongue grafting suitable for apple trees. Raffia and grafting wax seal the join.

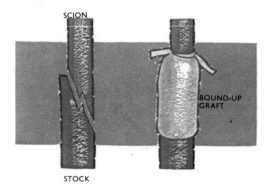

SCION

BOUND-UP GRAFT

STOCK

Grafting is usually done in early spring when the stocks are about eighteen months old. This is for producing large quantities of young trees for sale. Grafting can also be done with older trees to improve the fruiting or flowering. Budding is carried out in summer when the buds have developed properly and growth is vigorous.

Bush roses are budded on to briar stocks close to the root, and the upper part of the stock is removed later, so that all the shoots come from the new bud.

Standard roses are budded on to briars at the height required for the head of flowers.

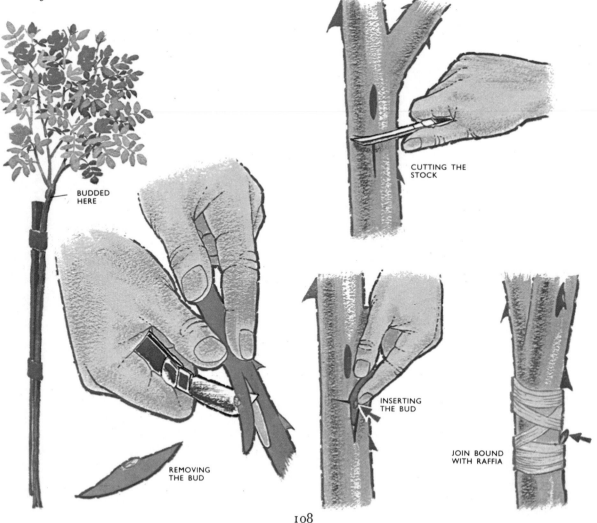

BUDDED HERE

CUTTING THE STOCK

REMOVING THE BUD

INSERTING THE BUD

JOIN BOUND WITH RAFFIA

CHAPTER SEVENTEEN

Weed Control

ALMOST every man-made habitat (e.g. hedgerow and gravel pit) has its typical weeds, but far the most important are the weeds of cultivated land. They compete with crops and reduce their yield. In the United States, a recent official estimate has put the combined cost of losses caused directly by weeds and the measures taken to control them at the staggering total of nearly four thousand million dollars.

In early times, and, indeed, until comparatively recent times, hand-pulling and hoeing were virtually the only ways available for killing weeds. These methods could only be used on a small scale and it was not until it became usual to sow crops in rows instead of broadcasting them that further progress could be made. In the 18th century, Jethro Tull, an Englishman, developed a horse-hoe which could be used to till between crops sown in rows. Since his time, the tractor has taken over from the horse and the techniques of weeding between rows have been greatly refined and improved. Such methods, however, can be used only in crops sown in wide rows, such as sugar beet, kale and some vegetables. Weeds between plants in the row have still to be removed by hand. Cereals are sown in rows too narrow to permit effective row tillage, and until chemical methods of controlling weeds were recently introduced, weeds were always a serious problem in these crops.

Typical crop rotations might include two or three consecutive cereal crops, under which weed populations would rise, and then a row crop, such as potatoes or sugar beet, which would be cultivated several times to kill weeds, and which was therefore regarded as a 'cleaning' crop. Such crops also tended to smother the weeds under their thick canopy of leaves. They greatly reduced weed populations and left the land in a clean and fertile state. The different times of sowing and cultivation of crops in a rotation in itself helps to reduce weeds by interrupting their growth rhythms.

There are two main classes of weeds: the rapid-growing annuals such as poppies, mayweeds and chickweeds, and the deep-rooted perennials, such as couch grass, thistles and bindweed. Unlike annual weeds, perennials can regenerate from their roots when their above-ground parts are cut off. This makes it hard to control them by normal cultivation methods, and where they had become a serious problem the farmer commonly resorted to *fallowing*. This entailed ploughing deeply in winter, followed by periodic cultivation (e.g. harrowing) during the season. The ploughing would bring to the surface much of the underground parts of the weeds, which could be killed by drying-out under the sun in summer, while the cultivations would induce the annual weeds to germinate, after which they could be killed by further cultivation.

Such fallowing means the loss of a crop for that season and is very expen-

Inter-row cultivating to keep down weeds in young sugar-beet.

sive. A much commoner practice is 'stubble cleaning'. This entails a light cultivation after harvest to induce as many weeds as possible to germinate. These die later in winter or are eventually buried by ploughing, before they have set seed.

The most striking advances in weed control, however, have been made by the discovery of chemicals which have the ability to destroy weeds and yet leave the crop intact. Certain chemicals, such as sulphuric acid and copper sulphate, have long been known to have *herbicidal* (plant-killing) properties under certain circumstances. It was not, however, until the discovery of the so-called *plant growth regulating compounds* in the 1940's that the real break-through came.

These compounds are closely related to certain growth hormones which occur naturally in plants and

Spraying potato tops with dilute sulphuric acid kills the tops so that lifting the crop is made easier.

The potato-lifter in action. The withered stems and leaves do not interfere.

The principle of selective action of sulphuric acid is that the cereal crop throws off the spray droplets while the weed leaves get covered and killed off.

which assist in regulating their growth. When applied in large enough amounts to the leaves, they enter and move in the sap to different parts of the plants, where they upset the natural processes of life, disrupt growth and eventually cause death.

Examples of these compounds are the chlorinated phenoxyacetic acids, of which the most commonly used to-day are *MCPA* (4-chloro-2-methyl-phenoxyacetic acid) and 2, 4-*D* (2, 4-dichlorophenoxyacetic acid).

Used at the proper dosage rate (usually between $\frac{1}{4}$ and 2 lb per acre) and at the proper stage of growth of the crop, these herbicides have the extremely important property of being *selective*. In this case, they are active against broad-leaved plants, but not against members of the grass family (such as the cereals). This means in practice that these compounds can be used to control many annual broad-leaved weeds in cereal crops and lawns. It was only com-

paratively recently that cereal crops yellow with charlock or red with poppies were a frequent and vivid sight. These two weeds are very susceptible to *MCPA* and 2, 4-*D* and can be completely controlled with them, so much so that fields containing much of either weed are nowadays comparatively rare. *MCPA* and 2, 4-*D* are to-day used on a world-wide scale and their total contribution to increased crop yields has been enormous.

In considering other types of herbicide, it is perhaps best to group them under the three principal ways in which they act.

The first group includes the so-called *contact herbicides*. We have already mentioned sulphuric acid; other examples are the dinitro compounds *DNOC* (3, 5-dinitro *ortho* cresol) and *dinoseb* (2, 4-dinitro-6-*sec*-butylphenol), and the new bipyridyl herbicides *diquat* (1, 1′-ethylene-2, 2′-bipyridylium) and *paraquat* (1, 1-dimethyl-4,

4'-bypyridylium). All these compounds kill those parts of the plant with which they come in contact and act very rapidly. They do not move through the sap into other parts of the plant. The dinitro compounds are effective against weeds in cereal crops and in peas and lucerne. Some scorching of crops is produced by these two chemicals. They are, however, very poisonous and their use is declining. The use of diquat, and especially paraquat, is increasing. They are comparatively non-poisonous and have the useful property of being broken down rapidly in the soil. Diquat is used for killing potato tops before lifting the tubers, while paraquat shows considerable promise for killing grass-land swards so that new seed can be sown without ploughing.

The next group of herbicides includes those which are commonly applied to the leaves and which are then *translocated* through the plant in its sap. *MCPA* and *2, 4-D* have already been mentioned. Other examples are the phenoxybutyric and phenoxypropionic compounds, which are ef-

The Devil's Lilac which has invaded many tropical rivers can be controlled to some extent by spraying with 2, 4-D.

fective against certain broad-leaved weeds, *dalapon* (2, 2-dichloropropionic acid) and *TCA* (trichloroacetic acid) which are active against grasses, and *amino triazole*, which is active against most plants.

The translocated herbicides are rather slow in action and for this reason are not used for *pre-emergence* application (i.e. against weeds appearing between sowing and emergence of the crop).

The last group of herbicides includes the *soil-acting herbicides*. This group is of increasing importance and includes many compounds. In general they are extremely insoluble and act through the roots rather than the leaves of plants. They are usually applied to bare soil, enter weed seedlings through the roots and kill them when they emerge from the soil surface. Examples are the triazine family of herbicides, the phenylurea and the phenyl carbamate families. The triazines provide an excellent example of selective action in the case of *simazine* (2-chloro-4, 6-bis-ethylamino-1, 3, 5-triazine) and maize. Maize, unlike most plants, has a mechanism for changing simazine, which is normally extremely poisonous to plants, into a harmless derivative. Thus simazine can be applied to maize at rates high enough to kill a whole range of annual weeds without damage to the crop. Simazine has made it possible to eliminate much of the cultivation usual to control weeds in maize, as well as eliminating weed competition at a time when the crop is young and liable to suffer severely in consequence. In general, compounds in this group are applied to the soil at

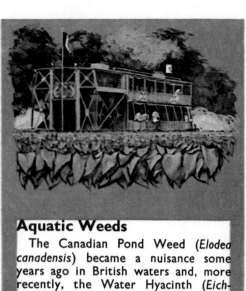

Aquatic Weeds

The Canadian Pond Weed (*Elodea canadensis*) became a nuisance some years ago in British waters and, more recently, the Water Hyacinth (*Eichhornia crassipes*) has been giving trouble in Africa. This plant has covered vast stretches of tropical rivers and large sums of money are being spent on its control. The plant exists as floating masses which may or may not be attached to the banks. The leaves stand clear of the water. Broken pieces rapidly grow into new plants and the infestation spreads, both naturally and by man's intervention.

Navigation is almost impossible on some of the more affected rivers. Fishing suffers and animals are unable to drink freely. As the leaves are above the surface, spraying with herbicides such as 2, 4-D is possible and effective. Completely submerged weeds are best controlled by mechanical cutting and dredging. Chemical treatment of rivers must not harm the fish or other animal life, nor must it endanger the drinking supply taken from the river lower down its course.

or shortly after the time the crop is sown, so that germinating weeds are killed, and the young crop has a clean start. As they are very insoluble, they tend to persist in the soil for a very long time—indeed, some will continue to control weeds for the whole season.

113

SBG—H

CHAPTER EIGHTEEN

Insecticides

IT is probably fair to assume that about 15% of the World's annual possible production is lost due to attack by insects. Damage occurs not only in the field but also in store where conditions are ideal for the development of pests such as grain weevils which infest stored cereals. If all these losses could be avoided the food saved would be sufficient for about 500 million people. The cost of control would be small compared with the enormous value of the material saved. Foodstuffs are not the only materials subjected to insect attack. Timber is frequently destroyed and Man himself is often plagued by insect-borne diseases. Obviously the control of insect pests is a vital aspect of Man's economy.

The term *insecticide* is applied to any substance used to kill or control insect pests but not all act in the same way. A number of mineral dusts such as silicon or aluminium compounds are occasionally used to kill insect pests in houses or stores. Their action is mechanical. Insects are covered with a waxy cuticle which makes them waterproof and prevents the loss of their body fluids. The sharp edges of the dust particles damage the cuticle and cause the insect to die from loss of water by evaporation. The majority of insecticides, however, act by chemical means. They interfere with the vital living processes of the insects, causing paralysis and eventual death.

Stomach poisons can act only when swallowed by the insects. They are useful therefore only when the insects' food can be treated. Locusts

Solid carbon dioxide (dry ice) is sprinkled among the sacks in a warehouse. This has some fumigant value but is normally used in conjunction with other fumigants.

and other biting insects can be controlled by applying insecticides to their food plants. The insecticide may damage the lining of the gut or may simply be absorbed into the body. Poison *baits* are sometimes used to control ants and cockroaches. An insecticide is added to an attractive food (bait) in the infested area and

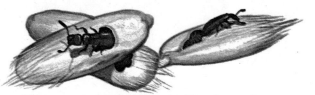

The young beetles live inside the grains of wheat and when full grown emerge leaving an empty husk. The grains with holes in are all empty.

Pyrethrum flowers are grown on a large scale in Kenya for the production of insecticide.

the pests die after taking the food. A more recent development is the *systemic insecticide*. Compounds of this type are stomach insecticides which are absorbed by *plants* and carried in the sap. They are thus active against the various sucking insects (e.g. *aphids*) which do not *eat* the leaves and are not affected by normal stomach insecticides. Stomach poisons are normally applied to growing crops as dusts or liquid sprays. Moth proofing of fabrics depends upon the impregnation with stomach poisons to kill clothes moths and other pests such as carpet beetles.

Contact poisons are insecticides which begin to act as soon as they make contact with any part of the insect. The speed of action depends partly on the ability of the insecticide to penetrate the insect cuticle and on the nature of the poison. Contact poisons can be applied in a number of ways. Household aerosols usually contain a mixture of compounds with contact action. The particles in the spray touch the insects and rapidly

Swellings (galls) on roots can cause serious losses to the crop unless action is taken to control the insects responsible.

affect them. Not all insecticides act with the same speed. One may 'knock-out' an insect quickly but allow it to recover later while other compounds act slowly but kill completely. Aerosols usually contain both forms and produce a quick '*knock down*' and a sure kill. Obviously a fine spray of this kind is suitable only when insects are actually present. Contact insecticides which are sprayed or dusted on the resting places of insects and remain active for a period of time are called *residual insecticides*. Houses in the tropics are frequently sprayed with residual insecticides to kill any mosquitoes which alight on the walls. Particles of insecticide penetrate the legs of the insect and act upon the nervous system or the respiratory mechanisms. The more volatile an insecticide (i.e. the more quickly it evaporates), the less effective it will be as a residual compound.

Fumigants are gaseous compounds which penetrate the infested material killing all the insect pests living in it. The space being fumigated must be sealed off to prevent escape of the poisonous gas. After a given time, which depends upon temperature, dose and type of fumigant used, etc., the covers are removed and the space is ventilated (making sure that people are kept away). The gas disperses gradually, leaving no living pests and no harmful residue. Fumigation, however, gives no lasting protection against insect attack and, once the gas has dispersed, new pests can enter if the material is left exposed. By treating the building structure with residual insecticide much of the re-infestation can be avoided. Valuable fumigants include *methyl bromide* (CH_3Br), *hydrogen cyanide* (HCN) and *carbon tetrachloride* (CCl_4). Fumigants are very dangerous gases and must be applied only by trained operators.

The Insecticidal Compounds

Until 25 years or so ago only a

few insecticidal compounds were in use. Most of these were plant products such as *derris* and *nicotine*. *Arsenic* compounds were widely used too but all these have the disadvantage that they are total poisons (i.e. they act against all animals). The ideal insecticide (which has not yet been found) would be lethal to a certain range of insects yet completely harmless to other forms of life. *Pyrethrins* – substances extracted from the pyrethrum flower – have been known for many years to be insecticidal. They produce a quick knock-down but are not always lethal. They are used in household aerosols and frequently on stored grain, for they have little effect on human beings at the doses used against insects. Investigations are continually being carried out to discover the 'perfect insecticide' and with the discovery of DDT in the 1930's it was thought to have been found. DDT (short for *dichloro-diphenyl-trichloroethane*) is a fairly simple artificial compound which is highly toxic to insects, is long lasting and in general not nearly so poisonous to mammals as many other insecticides. In fact it was thought that at the doses required to kill insects DDT was almost harmless to Man. However, DDT is stored by the body and continual ingestion of residues can be harmful. Although its action is slow, DDT is lethal to all insects and was applied in agricultural and medical spheres on a large scale. Soon after the discovery of DDT, *lindane* (benzene-hexa-chloride) was discovered

Small spraying machines such as this can be used for small areas. Tractor-mounted machines or helicopters are better for orchards and large tracts of land.

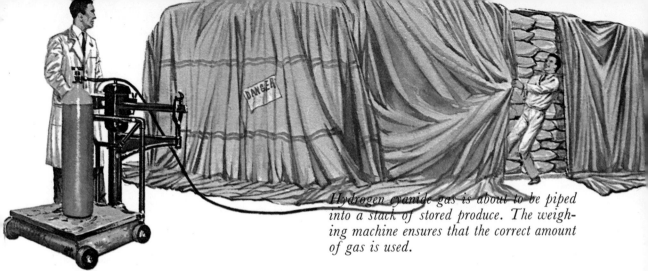

Hydrogen cyanide gas is about to be piped into a stack of stored produce. The weighing machine ensures that the correct amount of gas is used.

along with several other related compounds (e.g. *aldrin* and *dieldrin*). These are all *chlorinated hydro-carbons* (i.e. hydrocarbons in which some or all of the hydrogen has been replaced by chlorine). Many have useful properties as vapours but are especially valuable as sprays and dusts. All chlorinated hydrocarbons are stored in the fatty tissue of animals (including man) and can be lethal; therefore some have been officially banned.

As a result of the widespread use of DDT and other artificial insecticides many insects – e.g. house-flies and mosquitoes – have become *resistant* (i.e. they do not now succumb to a dose which may be many times stronger than one which would have killed the insects originally). Much work has been done on resistance and it appears that the insects have developed a chemical mechanism which destroys the poison before it does any harm. The problem has to be overcome by increasing the dose, by destroying the protective mechanism or by using another insecticide. The first is not practical as it may involve residues which are dangerous to other animals. The two other possibilities have stimulated much research and have resulted in the appearance of many new insecticides

of which the most important at present are the organic compounds of phosphorus such as *diazinon* and *malathion*. Resistance is developing, however, in many insect species and to many insecticides so that there is always a demand for new compounds.

Before an insecticide can be marketed safely it has to undergo a series of strict tests. It has to be active against insects at low doses. Other tests must be performed to see if there is any action against other animals or plants – especially after prolonged contact with residues – and to see if treated food is affected. After the small-scale laboratory tests, field tests must be performed on a fairly large scale to find out if its use is economical and practical. An important point is that in agricultural applications an insecticide should not kill beneficial insects as well as the pests. Insecticides should be *selective* in their actions. This is where biological control gains over insecticidal action. Biological control, using natural enemies, *is* selective although obviously slower than the insecticidal measures. There are no harmful residues after biological control and perhaps in future more attention will be paid to the possibilities of using biological rather than chemical control methods.

CHAPTER NINETEEN

Disease in Plants

EVERY year, huge quantities of crops are lost through disease. The study of these various ailments is, therefore, a very important branch of science and is called *plant pathology*. Plant diseases are almost as old as plants themselves, for clear signs of disease are shown in many ancient fossils. Cultivated plants, however, suffer far more than wild ones – largely because many plants of the same kind are grown closely together. In the wild, a plant is not always surrounded by others of the same kind and germs have less chance of spreading.

Until a few centuries ago, it was firmly believed that diseases were due to the 'wrath of the Gods'. This is still so in many primitive communities and elaborate ceremonies are performed to 'please the Gods'. In the 17th century

it was noticed that the weather seemed to affect the health of the crops. Mildews and other fungi were known to be associated with many diseased plants but it was believed that the fungi sprang up in the dying tissues. Not until the 19th century when Pasteur showed that living things could not arise from nothing, did people come to realize that the fungi actually caused the disease in many cases.

Fungi Causing Diseases

Fungi of one sort or another are the causes of the majority of plant diseases. Some diseases, such as the black-spotting of Sycamore leaves, do not appear to do much harm although every leaf may be affected. Others are more serious. *Potato Blight* – the disease that caused widespread famine in Europe (especially Ireland) in the

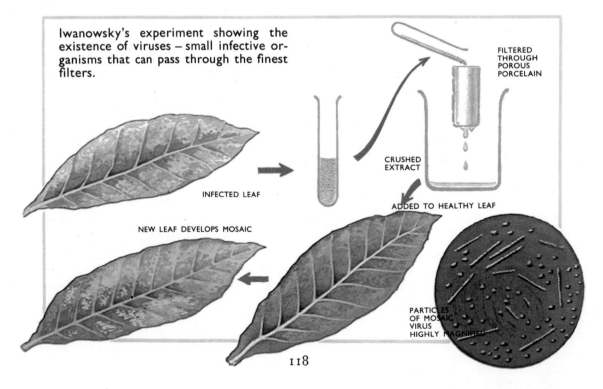

Iwanowsky's experiment showing the existence of viruses – small infective organisms that can pass through the finest filters.

FILTERED THROUGH POROUS PORCELAIN

CRUSHED EXTRACT

INFECTED LEAF

ADDED TO HEALTHY LEAF

NEW LEAF DEVELOPS MOSAIC

PARTICLES OF MOSAIC VIRUS HIGHLY MAGNIFIED

118

1840's – is a very serious disease and can rapidly destroy the whole plant. *Rusts* and *smuts* are important fungal diseases of cereals. 'Damping off' of seedlings is also caused by fungi, and results in collapse of the seedlings just above ground level.

The fungus body consists of a mass of fine threads called *hyphae* (high-fee). These threads get into the plant through injuries, through the leaf pores or even through undamaged cuticles. The threads then divide and branch through the tissues of the host, absorbing food materials. Blemishes and discolorations appear on the plant and these are often the sites of spore production. Spores are tiny one-celled bodies which can float in the air and spread to other plants where they grow into new fungus threads.

Many fungus diseases thrive best in damp conditions. Potato Blight is a good example and it is far more common, for instance, in Ireland, where the climate is damper, than in Eastern England. The early idea that bad weather caused disease was not so far off the mark after all.

Bacteria and Viruses

As the investigation of plant diseases progressed, it was found that some diseases were not associated with fungi. It was suggested that bacteria might be involved. These tiny organisms were already known to produce disease in animals, although the majority are harmless – and often useful – organisms. Many rots of fruit and vegetables are now known to be caused by bacteria. The organisms invade the tissues and break them down by enzyme action into a watery, smelly mess.

Even after the discovery of bacterial disease, still other diseases appeared to have no associated germs. Pasteur suggested that there might be even

Streaked wallflower and Potato-leaf roll – two virus diseases that are transmitted by aphids that suck plant juices (below).

smaller 'germs'. He was right and these minute 'germs' are called *viruses*. Their existence was first demonstrated by a Russian scientist called Iwanowsky in the 1890's. He took some juice from a tobacco plant suffering from a disease called *mosaic*. The juice was filtered through porcelain fine enough to remove even the smallest bacteria and was then smeared on a fresh tobacco plant. Mosaic appeared, showing that whatever causes the disease can pass through the finest filters.

CLUSTERS OF
SPORES ON BARBERRY

Black Rust of wheat, caused by the fungus *Puccinia graminis*. The black streaks are formed by masses of black spores breaking through the surface (below). There are several stages in the life cycle, including two stages on barberry leaves (right).

Potato blight on leaves and tuber. The disease starts in an infected tuber and spreads to the leaves. From there, spores produced in the mildewy regions spread to other plants.

SPORE-BEARING
BRANCHES
BREAKING THROUGH
LEAF SURFACE

Club-root on a cabbage plant. The fungus causes giant cells to develop in the roots (below). The plant then begins to wilt.

A potato-tuber infected with the fungus of Wart Disease (*Synchytrium endobioticum*).

SPORES DEVELOPING IN WART TISSUE. THEY ARE RELEASED WHEN THE TISSUES DECAY.

Since then, hundreds of viruses have been discovered. They cause serious diseases in both plants and animals. The virus bodies have been isolated and examined with electron microscopes. They are minute particles about 20 milli-microns across – 50 thousand would not stretch across a pinhead. Viruses consist of a nucleic acid and protein. They can be crystallized like chemical compounds, yet, when injected into a host, they multiply like bacteria. In plants, viruses frequently produce a mottling (mosaic) of the leaves or flowers. The food-making ability of the leaves is reduced and the plant often becomes spindly. There is a serious loss of yield. Potatoes suffer from a number of serious virus diseases such as leaf-mosaic and leaf-roll.

Other Causes of Disease

A few diseases are caused by protozoans and by nematode worms that get into the tissues. Symptoms include galls and stunted growth. Some insects cause disease-like symptoms by injecting poisonous substances into the plant. The symptoms often resemble those of virus diseases but are not so persistent, and recovery is common.

Physiological diseases are serious but easily remedied. They result from the lack of some food material – it may be a trace-element such as boron that is required in minute quantities, or it may be something like phosphate that is needed in larger amounts. Soil analysis soon gives the answer and addition of the missing element or elements cures the trouble.

Transmission and Control of Plant Diseases

It is rarely practical (or even possible) to cure a diseased plant. Control is based on *prevention*. The golden rule for gardeners dealing with a diseased plant is 'dig it up and burn it'. Only in this way can the germs be completely destroyed. However, before the diseases can be controlled, it is necessary to know how they are transmitted from plant to plant. It is useless to treat the seed if infection is transmitted by insects. Nor is there any use in controlling insects if the disease germs lurk in the soil from year to year. Many diseases, however, pass to other plants in more than one way.

Soil-borne diseases – such as *Clubroot* of cabbages and *Wart Disease* of potatoes – pass from plant to plant by means of spores resting in the soil. The spores are released into the soil and remain there, waiting for another crop to attack. Many of the soil-borne diseases – mainly caused by nematodes, fungi and bacteria – can be avoided by rotating crops. The spores perish before a susceptible crop is returned to the land. Some fungi, however, including those causing clubroot and wart disease, have very long-lived spores and crop-rotation will not necessarily avoid these diseases. Some varieties of potato are immune to wart disease and these can be used safely where the disease is known to exist. Indeed it is an offence to plant non-immune varieties in such regions.

A number of diseases are transmitted from one crop to the next by means of seed or other reproductive bodies (e.g. tubers). Fungus diseases are commonly transmitted in and on seeds. They can be avoided to some extent by treating the seed with fungicide (fungus-killer) before planting. The dangers of seed dressings and other crop protection chemicals are, however, becoming more and more apparent with the serious decline in wildlife. Virus diseases rarely pass on in the seed but commonly do so in tubers, bulbs and cuttings. Potato viruses pass on in the tubers and, within a few years, the virus population may be so high as to make the plants useless. Fresh, virus-free tubers should be planted each year. The viruses are initially transmitted from plant to plant by various aphids (greenfly). These are absent or rare in cool regions and the disease is absent. Tubers from these regions are used as 'seed' in other regions. Although the plants may become infected during growth, they will produce a reasonably good crop. Fresh, virus-free tubers must be obtained again for the following year, however.

Even when clean, disease-free seed is planted in clean land, diseases can still be contracted. Air-borne spores from neighbouring crops can cause heavy infection. Potato blight and wheat rust are two major air-borne diseases, caused by fungi. The growing of resistant varieties helps to overcome disease. Keeping down weeds that might harbour the germs is important and the use of 'clean' seed is essential. If only a few seeds are infected, a disease can later spread from these plants to the whole field. When effective fungus-killing compounds are known, they should be sprayed or dusted onto the plants to kill fungus spores *before they are able to get into the plant.*

Of the insect-borne diseases, viruses are the most important. They are frequently carried by aphids that suck up sap. The viruses get into the saliva and are then injected into the next plant at the next meal. Usually only one or a few species of insect can transmit a particular virus and if the insect can be controlled, the virus disease will also be controlled.

CHAPTER TWENTY

Biological Control

IN the wild, plants tend to spread randomly over a wide area – their distribution is patchy. Modern methods of farming concentrate crops in well-defined areas and in time. The more intensive that farming becomes the greater are the 'spoils' for insects and other pests; the easier it is for them to find a source of food and, consequently, the better are the conditions for reproduction.

Food is not only grown in a concentrated way; the harvested crops and their products are stored in large quantities – granaries hold millions of bushels of wheat and warehouses are full of flour and other foodstuffs. Besides providing pests with a vast amount of readily available food man also encourages their spread by carrying them from their natural homes to other parts in road vehicles, ships (particularly those carrying edible cargoes), trains and other forms of transport.

Apart from the chemical control of

The spread of prickly pear cacti has been controlled in Australia by the moth, Cactoblactis cactorum, *the caterpillars of which bore through the stems of the cacti weakening them.*

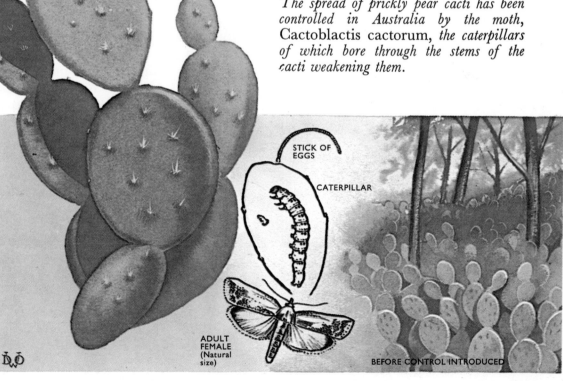

STICK OF EGGS

CATERPILLAR

ADULT FEMALE (Natural size)

BEFORE CONTROL INTRODUCED

The ladybird, Rodolia cardinalis, *has successfully controlled the Fluted scale insect,* Icerya purchasi, *a pest of orange trees in California. Adults and larvae are predators.*

pests, another of the methods used in the control of both animal and plant pests is termed *biological control.* This involves the use of a pest's natural enemies to keep it under control.

Perhaps the first really successful use of biological control was in the almost complete extermination of the Fluted scale insect, a bug which caused great damage to the orange trees in the Californian citrus groves. This pest first appeared there in 1868 having been accidentally introduced from Australia on imported acacias. Its numbers quickly reached pest proportions. C. V. Riley made a careful study of the insect. He found that in its native land it was held in check by its natural enemies. Its activities never reached pest propor-

tions. Several of the insect's enemies were sent to the United States of America and in a series of carefully controlled experiments the larvae of a species of ladybird successfully cleared a test tree of the pest. The predatory beetles rapidly increased in numbers spreading over the orange groves. Within a few years from the time of their introduction in 1889 the pest was brought under control and the industry was saved from impending disaster. Today the Fluted scale insect is no longer a major pest in the U.S.A., but a stock of ladybirds is maintained so that any local outbreaks of the pest can quickly be controlled. To date such measures have always been successful.

This particular example of the application of biological control is a near perfect one. Almost the first of the pest's enemies to be experimented with proved successful as a means of control and there have been no side effects such as the beetles themselves becoming pests.

Before discussing further successful examples it is as well to consider the problems of the scientist in looking for the most suitable natural enemy of a particular pest. There are many examples of a control having been introduced without proper care. A plague of caterpillars in parts of New York was stripping the trees of their leaves. The introduction of sparrows from Europe removed the caterpillars. But sparrows are also seed-eaters competing with others for food and very soon had themselves become pests driving many of the American birds from their natural homes.

Will the control itself become a pest? The possibility of this happening is very real and so the life history and the habits of the proposed control factor must be thoroughly worked out.

In new surroundings an animal will often extend its activities. It may therefore come across food that it finds more desirable. Even in its natural home its likings may change, particularly as farming spreads. The Colorado beetle is an excellent example of such a change in taste. At one time this beetle was harmless. Its natural food consisted of the burrs of some wild plants. With the spread of potato farming, however, it began to feed on the potato plants. In this case both the larvae and the adults found their new food palatable. By changing their diet and their home they also appear to have avoided the parasites that previously held them in check. So the Colorado beetle multiplied rapidly and has, of course, caused great loss to the potato industry. No biological control has been found to combat the beetle. It is controlled largely by chemical means and also by the strict inspection of imported crops.

The food tastes of an imported pest may change – either because its natural supply of food is in short supply or because it finds another more palatable food source. The change may take it out of reach of an animal used as a control, for the latter may not spread with the pest. Its introduction will be useless therefore.

Many insects have been used as biological control agents. It is usually, but not always, the larva that does the control work. The adult usually eats different food and, although the larva eats a pest, the adult may itself become a pest. Such problems must be investigated before introducing biological control.

Another factor of considerable importance in limiting the application of biological control is climate. If the control is introduced into a warmer country its life cycle may not be speeded up to the same extent as that of the host (the converse may also apply). Thus as soon as the life cycles of host and parasite are out of step the latter will be ineffective. This can be partly overcome by finding a control that has an adaptable life cycle.

There are records of devastating effects of plagues of locusts in very early writings. Control is largely by chemical means but a parasitic fungus gives a certain degree of natural control. Several locusts are shown dying from a fungal attack.

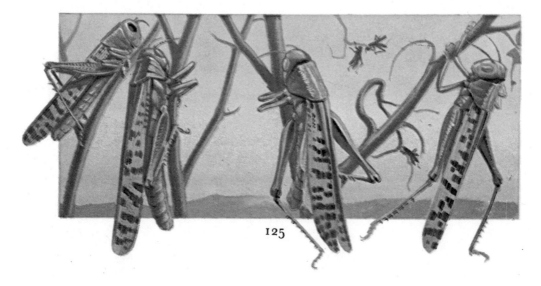

The Japanese beetle (top left) *has been partly controlled by a roundworm. Sugar cane weevils* (top right) *have been controlled in Hawaii by a species of fly. Attempts are still being made in the United States to control the Gypsy moth.*

Many insects parasitize others. This Sphinx moth caterpillar is covered with the cocoons of a parasitic wasp.

The success of applying biological control to the citrus grove problem in California encouraged biologists to look for insects that might control pests in other places. Attempts in Fiji have met with outstanding success. The Levuana coconut moth appears to be controlled permanently and possibly may be eradicted. In Hawaii the sugar cane industry was badly affected by a weevil, the larvae of which bored into the cane. The introduction of a species of fly quickly suppressed the pest's activities.

It is significant that in these instances success was met with where small island groups were concerned. The biological control of pests has not been obtained over large areas or to any great extent in the colder parts of the world.

The best example of the control of plant pests is the campaign against cacti such as prickly pear. These grow naturally in North and South America but were introduced into Australia as ornamental garden plants. By about 1925 these cacti had spread to such an extent that they covered over 90,000 square miles.

A large number of insects that live on cacti were experimented with in an attempt to bring the cacti under control. Eventually a moth-borer, *Cactoblactis cactorum*, native to Argentina, was thought to be suitable. It was released in Australia and very quickly the larvae destroyed large numbers of the plants by boring into and weakening them. This not only stopped it spreading further but actually reduced the area infected.

This example also illustrates how complicated are the relationships between the animals and plants of a community and what great problems exist in choosing a suitable controlling agent. In South Africa the insecticide (i.e. the more quickly it evaporates), the less effective it will be as a residual compound.

In considering the use of biological control account must be taken of the cost of such a venture. Ideally it must be no more expensive than chemical or other means of control (though two or more methods are often used together). To keep local and spasmodic outbreaks of a pest under control it has been found necessary to keep stocks of the controlling agent in readiness. The equipment and the staff needed for this is expensive – and the controls need food! In an attempt to overcome the latter problem work is proceeding on the making of suitable artificial foods.

A species of ladybird beetle, however, has been reared successfully by feeding it and its larva on the Citrus mealy bug that the larva controls. The pest can be fed on potato sprouts – a cheap form of food.

Reports from Italy suggest that a tiny chalcid, *Prospaltella berlesei*, has brought the Mulberry scale, *Diaspis pentagona*, under control and thus has saved the silk industry in Italy.

The United States of America undoubtedly suffers more from the ravages of pests, particularly insects, than any other country. Nearly a hundred species of insects imported into the U.S.A. as controls have become established. A number of these were imported from Europe to control various forest pests such as the Gypsy moth, and the European corn-borer and scale insects.

Bacteria, fungi, viruses, protozoa and roundworms have also been employed for biological controls. No great success has been obtained using bacteria but recent experiments are more hopeful. A virus – that causing the disease Myxomatosis in rabbits – was successfully used in Australia to control an enormous population of rabbits. One example of the successful use of fungi comes from Canada. An apple sucker has been controlled by the fungus *Entomophthora sphaerosperma*. Satisfactory results have also been obtained in some cases in Florida and various scale insects have been suppressed by spraying the spores of the Red-headed fungus and White-headed fungus on insect-infested trees.

Some success has been obtained in controlling the Japanese beetle with a roundworm. It has destroyed large numbers of the beetle grubs in some areas.

It is very difficult to evaluate the success of biological control in specific examples. Even when a pest's numbers are controlled or reduced it is possible that other natural factors have had some effect. However, the evidence is such that it has proved its usefulness in a number of cases and it may play an important part in the control of pests.

Index